ANTIQUE STEINS

A COLLECTORS' GUIDE

ANTIQUE STEINS
A COLLECTORS' GUIDE

James R. Stevenson
Photographs by Robert C. Hogan

New York • *CORNWALL BOOKS* • *London*

Cornwall Books
440 Forsgate Drive
Cranbury, New Jersey 08512

Cornwall Books
25 Sicilian Avenue
London WC1A 2QH, England

Cornwall Books
Unit 1, 2133 Royal Windsor Drive
Mississauga, Ontario
Canada L5J 1K5

SECOND PRINTING

Library of Congress Cataloging in Publication Data

Stevenson, James R., 1939–
    Antique steins.

    Bibliography: p.
    Includes index.
    1. Steins—Collectors and collecting.   I. Title.
NK4695.S73S76   745.1   80-70730
ISBN 0-8453-4708-X   AACR2

Printed in the United States of America

Contents

*for the members of Die Studenten Prinz Gruppe
of Stein Collectors International, who
represent the camaraderie and fellowship
that all stein collectors can enjoy*

Preface

I have felt for years that an excellent resource book was needed for beginning stein collectors. I wasn't quite certain how I would be able to obtain photographs of steins but knew I could provide other information to collectors. After I had discussed the idea of a book with my colleague and photographer, Robert Hogan, we experimented with the photography. Finally, after months, we felt we could take high-quality photographs of steins, and we proceeded to organize our project.

We have tried to cover three areas of stein collecting in the book. First, we have provided excellent photographs of steins. Second, we have included prices so that collectors and dealers will have guidelines. Third, we have provided practical information about stein collecting.

Many of us appreciate steins for their aesthetic beauty. This book should confirm this belief and provide direction for collectors who seek out these fine objets d'art.

Finally, I wish to point out that there are other stein books available. This book is written to supplement other books. Collectors should avail themselves of all published literature if they wish to enhance their knowledge of steins. This book will fill certain gaps and will show that more research should be done in the area of antique steins.

Acknowledgments

There are many individuals I wish to thank for assisting me in the preparation of this book. Les and Charlotte Whitham were of great help with the editing and, along with my wife, Marie, provided direction and ideas. Members of the Student Prince Chapter of Stein Collectors International gave me the initial support and encouragement that got the book off the ground. Numerous collectors and dealers allowed me to photograph steins from their collections. Many throughout the country assisted me with the stein prices and helped complete the survey for the book.

I am grateful to Pat Clark and Jack Lowenstein for allowing me to use their translations for the Mettlach titles I used in the descriptions of these steins. I am indebted to John O'Connor and Pat Clark for allowing me to use the information from their *Prosit* article of June 1977 in describing the Mettlach occupational steins.

I would also like to thank, in alphabetical order, the following individuals for their contributions:

Sam Brainard	Al Kleindienst
William and Nancy Burkle	Ray Lasky
Paul Cantin	Ron Olson
Leo Cashatt	Frank and Diane Pociadlo
James DeMars	Fred Roschow
Toini Ganley	Leonard Schenk
Michael Guy	Fred Schroeder
Irving Johnsen	Al and Barbara Statkum

Stein Terminology

THUMBLIFT

TANG

INLAY

HINGE PIN

LID

HINGE

SHANK

STRAP SUPPORT

HANDLE

STRAP

PANEL

BODY

HOLLOW BASE

Manufacturers and Marks

Beuler, Karl: artist employed by the Girmscheid factory in Höhr-Grenzhausen at the turn of the century. This mark usually found on the body of the stein.

Capo-di-monte: mark used by factory in Naples in late eighteenth century and early nineteenth century. Other factories were also established and used this mark on their porcelain steins after 1820. (See *Prosit*, March 1976, article by John A. Ey, Jr.)

DRGM (Deutsches Reichs Gebrauchmuster): means the design of the stein is patented. Steins with this mark are dated pre-1918.

Gerz, Simon Peter: company in Höhr-Grenzhausen founded in mid-nineteenth century; still producing steins today.

Gesetzlich geschützt: means the design of the stein is protected by law or patented.

GESETZLICH GESCHÜTZT

Girmscheid: factory founded in Höhr-Grenzhausen in later nineteenth-century and still producing steins today.

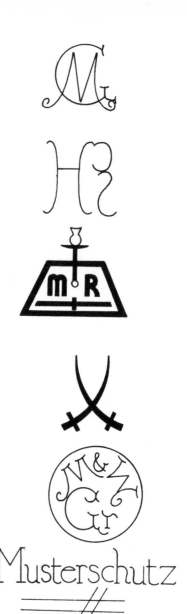

HR: possibly the mark of Herman Roch, who left Villeroy and Boch to establish his own firm in Mettlach. (See *Keramik* by Theresa Thomas.) It may also be that of Hauber & Reuther of Freising. (See *HR Steins* by Mike Wald.)

Marzi and Remy: factory founded in 1879 and is still producing steins.

Mayer, Joseph: signature found on character steins mostly at turn of century.

Meissen: factory founded in or near Dresden in 1710. A number of versions of the crossed-swords mark were used during the nineteenth century.

Merkelbach & Wick: factory founded in 1872; now known as Wick Werke. Mark used until 1921.

Musterschutz: means the stein is patented or protected by law. The hash mark (#) often appears with it.

Pauson, Martin: signature found on character steins made in Munich mostly at turn of century.

Reinemann, J.: signature found on character steins made in Munich mostly at turn of century.

Reinhold Merkelbach: firm founded in mid-nineteenth century and still producing steins today. This mark was used between 1870 and 1933.

Royal Vienna: mark used by many factories in Dresden area. One shown is that of the Ackerman & Fritsche Co. at Rudolstadt-Volkstedt, Germany from 1908 to 1912 (See *Prosit*, September 1975, article by John A. Ey, Jr.)

Thewalt, Albert Jacob: factory founded in 1893 and still producing steins in Höhr-Grenzhausen.

Villeroy and Boch at Mettlach: firm founded in 1841 and still producing steins today. *Left*, the Abbey of Mettlach (castle); *right*, Mercury mark.

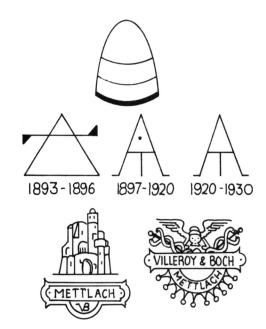

1

Introduction

It appears that beer drinking has a bright future as Americans and Europeans continue to increase their consumption. For centuries people have been interested in drinking beer and in producing appropriate drinking vessels for it. The first stein dates back hundreds of years to the sixteenth century, and most historians agree that the Germans deserve credit for inventing it.

Records exist for early steins, and in the sixteenth century the Germans legislated that all steins must be covered with lids to protect their contents from flies. One can theorize that the interest in beer and the popularity of beer drinking as a social phenomenon had led steins to be made in a variety of sizes and shapes.

Germany has an abundance of easily available clay, and the early stoneware and pottery steins were handmade. The early Kreussen pottery steins, made in the seventeenth century, were fire red and coated with a brown glaze. They were not particularly attractive. Later in the seventeenth century and during the eighteenth century, raised or relief designs appeared, more color was added, and the vessels generally became more attractive. You may have to visit a museum to view these early steins. Unfortunately, many collectors have only nineteenth-century reproductions of them, and it requires the expertise of a Kreussen historian to distinguish the genuine article from a copy.

Once the beauty of steins became recognized, interest in making them spread. During the eighteenth century, steins were made throughout Europe. The most productive period in the history of stein making, and the period of greatest interest in them, occurred in the second half of the nineteenth century when the Mettlach steins were produced.

Beauty and art appear in steins made from many kinds of materials—glass, salt glaze pottery, porcelain, silver, pewter, copper, ivory, stoneware, and faience. True collectors appreciate the art and recognize quality in steins regardless of the material of which they are made or the factories in which they were produced. A high-quality stein is collected for its intrinsic value as well as its investment potential.

Steins produced in Germany and Europe during the 1800s are beautiful for many reasons. The detailed work in the Mettlach etched steins is truly great art and must be compared to great paintings. Some of these steins depict figures of individuals singing, hunting, drinking, dancing, bowling, riding horses, or courting. So-called character steins are appreciated for their expressions—imagine a happy turnip or a sad radish, a drunken monkey, a gentleman fox, a smiling Munich child, a grinning monk, or a wise owl.

The fine quality and workmanship also appear in porcelain and ivory steins, with their stunning and detailed relief. Human figures and animals in many pewter relief steins are exceptional for their realism. Many hand-painted steins depicting military, occupational, and other scenes also exhibit high quality.

Some early glass steins, particularly the hand-blown color pieces with etched scenes in the body, are also excellent works. The amber brown, ruby red, green blown, cranberry, and cobalt blue are particularly pleasing. Many collectors purchase glass steins with hand-painted lids and display them by turning the open steins upside down on a shelf so that the lids will hang over the edge for easier viewing.

Royal Vienna, Meissen, and Capo-di-monte steins offer unusual examples of porcelain artistry and have become the speciality of many sophisticated collectors. The number of these steins available is limited, and most are in the hands of a few collectors and museums. Their prices are high and will continue to climb as collectors recognize their importance in the art world.

Many companies began producing steins in the nineteenth century, and most collector steins available in the market today were made in the later nineteenth and early twentieth centuries. Manufacturers often marked the steins under the base, usually by engraving. The steins usually collected in this category are Villeroy and Boch, HR, Merkelbach and Wick, Reinhold Merkelbach, Albert Jacob Thewalt, Simon Peter Gerz, and Marzi and Remy

It should be noted that the so-called Mettlach steins were actually produced by the firm of Villeroy and Boch in the small German town of Mettlach. They were stamped with the "castle" mark, which depicts a chapel built by monks in the tenth century A.D.

Many other stein manufacturers existed, but since their volumes were limited and they did not mark their steins, the company names are largely unknown.

Numerous stein factories stamped or engraved the words *Musterschutz* or *gesetzlich geschützt* under the base, which simply meant that the particular design of the **stein was** patented or protected by law. Other companies were not allowed to duplicate the stein. *Musterschutz* is found mainly on porcelain character steins; *gesetzlich geschützt* is found on many types of steins. Numerous steins also have *Germany* engraved or stamped under the base, which indicates that they were produced after 1892 when German law mandated this imprint for exported pieces. It is interesting that many unmarked steins (production-line workers simply missed them) can be identified by other characteristics, such as the quality of the etching, interior linings, body designs, and lids. Many unmarked steins can, almost without doubt, be attributed to Villeroy and Boch, HR, or some other particular company because of such identifying characteristics.

Beginning collectors should realize that up to the mid-nineteenth century, steins were apt to be unique because they were made to order in many cases. After this time, steins were mass-produced. No company records are available to indicate how many steins of one type were manufactured. The original catalogs supply much information about sizes, types of lids, prices, and so forth, but it is impossible to determine how many copies of a particular stein were made. In some cases, as with Mettlach 2002, the style was very popular and thousands were made; others, like Mettlach 2718, were very expensive and were limited in production. No one knows how many copies of this Mettlach stein were produced, but it is rarely seen today. This difference in availability today accounts for the price differential between 2002 and 2718.

The quality of steins varied over the years, and the collector with a keen eye can often identify steins that were expensive when they were made. Steins were made for everyone and could be purchased for less than one mark or as much as thirty marks ($7.50) for the seven-liter 1161 Mettlach stein. Other high-priced Mettlach steins were the St. Florian (DM 6,80) and the David and Goliath (DM 8,00). (In 1910 one U.S. dollar equaled four German marks.) The quality and size determined the price. The porcelain character steins were also expensive. The famous Musterschutz "stag" porcelain stein mended as many as ten molds together, and this required fine craftsmanship. It surely demanded a high price, although I have not been able to find original prices for Musterschutz character steins.

Most steins that were expensive at the time they were manufactured remain high-priced today. In purchasing Mettlachs, the stein collector can refer to the *Villery and Boch 1885/Mettlach 1905* catalog, published by Hans J. Ammelounx, and use the original prices for guidelines. There are exceptions, but as a rule of thumb, expensive steins have held their value in today's market.

2

Stein Collectors

Collectors of any sort are interesting, but it is difficult to label the characteristics of a collector, whether of steins, antiques, or any of the thousands of other collectibles on the market today. Profession or occupation is not relevant in describing a stein collector. There are doctors, lawyers, salesmen, educators, automobile mechanics, business executives, butchers—the list could go on indefinitely. Hence, the income range is great among stein collectors, and, as everyone is aware, one's ability to purchase is certainly limited by income.

A stein collector has an interest in accumulating. It would be unfair to say that he or she is a greedy person, but many collectors are concerned with quantity. Stein collectors are often mysterious. They hesitate to reveal themselves and will not let another collector into their personal lives until a certain period of time elapses and they feel the person can be trusted. This behavior is justified to some degree. One has only to read the daily newspaper to see that thefts of objets d'art in homes have increased and that the stein collector is a potential victim. It is relatively easy to sell stolen merchandise quickly for cash, and steins are among the items easily resold. Over the years, this author has seen many lists of stolen steins in newspapers and journals.

Stein collectors are frequently active in pursuit of their hobby. They often travel great distances to view or purchase steins. I have taken one-day trips of hundreds of miles to purchase one stein. I have had collectors from other regions of the country stay overnight at my home as they pursued steins at auctions, and many collectors refuse to let the necessity of extensive travel stand in the way of their making a purchase. Some time ago, a collector flew to an auction, purchased the Mettlach Black Forest stein, wrapped it in a case he had had specially made for it, and immediately left for home to enjoy his new acquisition.

The author inspecting a stein.

Holding stein correctly for inspection.

Stein collectors are sometimes peculiar and unfriendly. Recently, at an auction in Massachusetts, I sat across the aisle from a collector who had outbid me on two character nun porcelain steins at a New Hampshire auction a year earlier. He and his wife had been observed at other auctions purchasing steins. As the auction was about to begin, I asked him if he was enjoying his nun steins. He boldly replied to me that he didn't collect steins and proceeded to turn forward with an unfriendly, stern expression, apparently offended that someone was now aware of his hobby. Later during the auction, he leaned over to me and indicated that he did collect steins but made it clear that he didn't want anyone to know about this. I assured him that I would keep it a secret. Apparently, his wife had told him not to be so rude to me, so he decided at least to try to compensate for his earlier attitude.

Two New England collectors I know keep their steins wrapped in boxes and store them rather than display them. This is unusual; the practice of storing steins is not common among collectors. However, as with any group of hobbyists, there are unusual individuals who actually defeat the real purpose of collecting.

Stein collectors are bargain hunters. They do not like to pay retail prices for steins. Every collector at some time pays the going price, but only because other steins purchased have been cheaper and partially offset this decision. Retail prices on steins are determined by monitoring the prices for which steins are sold through auctions, dealers, and antique shows. Collectors keep personal records of these sales and also consult price books. Normally, a range of prices is available on a stein, and collectors use all this information as guidelines.

There is a feeling of conquest if one is able to purchase a good stein cheaply. We brag to our colleagues of how successful we were. The collector somehow feels that he has been able to outsmart the retailer and even a fellow collector, particularly if the purchase is made at an auction.

One collector saw a stein priced at fifty dollars in an antique shop. Upon looking this Musterschutz porcelain character over carefully and noticing its perfect condition, he asked the dealer if she could do any better on the price. She indicated that she would accept forty-five dollars. The collector wrote a check immediately and quickly evacuated the area. The retail price of the stein at the time was $300, but being a true collector and recognizing the opportunity to "steal" it, he asked for the best price available. We have all done this at one time or another.

Some stein collectors may not be completely reliable. "White lies" are dominant in the stein-collecting business as in any other. Anyone who has ever sold steins has probably stretched the truth at one time or another. We might indicate to a buyer that we paid a certain price for a stein and are only trying to make a few dollars or get our money back. It is not uncommon for a collector to sell a stein to a colleague and indicate that he is only making thirty-five dollars on it, while in actuality he is making seventy. Basically, the collectors I have met over the years have been honest, decent people, but when buying and selling enter the relationship an element of caution is necessary, and doubts arise as to how much profit one really is making in a sale.

Some collectors and dealers are dishonest about the condition of steins. Every collector has heard numerous stories about such situations. Recently a colleague warned me not to purchase a stein from a particular individual who has been selling expensive pieces, mostly Mettlachs, with repaired and replaced tops. If defects are recognized after a purchase, he claims ignorance and, in most cases, accepts the stein back, but many purchasers haven't noticed that these steins have been tampered with and have incorporated them into their collections.

I once had such an experience as a seller. The buyer returned a military stein to me, asserting that the original top had been replaced. There are still various opinions on the top, but the stein now remains in my private collection. If it is sold at a future date, it will be sold as a stein having a questionable pewter top, and the buyer will be aware of its questionable status. I made an honest mistake and have since learned that selling military steins is a delicate process. It takes a great deal of experience and expertise, and it's best to avoid getting involved unless one is knowledgeable about military steins.

Just two years ago, I returned a military stein to a dealer after seeing its picture in the reproduction section of June Dimsdle's book *Steins and Prices*. The dealer took the stein back. Maybe it was an honest mistake, but I will make no more purchases of military steins from that dealer.

A collector recently sent me a letter stating that he was insulted that I would offer less than his asking price for a stein. He had listed two steins for sale at prices that were excessive, but I was interested in one of them and made an offer of 10 percent less than the asking price. The collector indicated to me in his letter that he would never offer a collector less than the asking price. His overpriced steins were not purchased, and it is unlikely that any further communications with this person will be useful.

A collector in the South recently replied to an ad inserted in the *Antique Trader* and wrote for a list of steins for sale. He offered $325 for a perfect Mettlach stein noted in my list for $495. The collector indicated that he wanted high-quality Mettlachs in mint condition. The letter was somewhat aggravating to me, but rather than respond negatively, I mailed no response.

If you are selling steins, be prepared for low offers on your finest pieces. Everyone wishes to buy right, and this can make selling frustrating. You may label many collectors bold and aggressive, but perhaps they are just good business people. It is best to be fair or reasonable because most collectors know the value of their steins. Antique dealers and auctioneers are also becoming familiar with the stein market, but the stein "hawk" has a better opportunity to purchase at a good price in this market. Buying from noncollectors who have steins can also be an excellent opportunity, but even this group is becoming familiar with stein values. Often steins are greatly overpriced, and one must be constantly aware of this, since emotions and opportunity can overcome good sense.

3

Philosophies of Collecting

Collectors vary in their philosophies and reasons for collecting. There are as many philosophies as there are collectors. Jack Lowenstein, in an article in *Prosit* (September 1978), writes that people collect steins for three basic reasons: (1) nostalgia, (2) the compulsion to accumulate, and (3) the desire to amass negotiable wealth. I agree with these three explanations. I have met numerous collectors over the years and discussed their philosophies with them in person. Others have expressed their motives in letters and phone calls. The points of view differ widely, but the three reasons offered by Lowenstein are common to many collectors.

Collectors usually change their approaches and hence their types of purchases over a period of years. Mostly this is because they become more informed and sophisticated. Most of us start collecting steins by purchasing the cheaper ones. We think we are getting extravagant when we move to the fifty-dollar range. Then, as we read books, and see more steins, and discuss stein collecting with our colleagues, we realize that we are neophytes in a professional business.

What usually happens is that an individual begins by buying ten- or twenty-dollar pottery steins and then either is given or purchases an expensive one. I received a call once from a friend who saw me buy a pottery stein at an auction for eleven dollars and asked if I were interested in two Mettlachs. After twenty-four hours of hasty researching, I made the decision to purchase them. This meant an investment of over one hundred dollars in the two PUG 1909 series dwarf-scene Mettlachs. They still sit on my shelf as a reminder of the beginning.

Many collectors purchase only Mettlach steins because they feel that this insures that they are getting quality, a limited-edition item, and an investment that will appreciate. Some are narrow-minded and will not consider other steins

Stein display.   Stein display.

for their collections. Some buy other steins but only with the intent to trade or sell them for Mettlachs.

Military-stein specialists are a unique group, but they have become numerous. In fact, the interest in military steins has been so great that John Harrell has recently published his second book on military steins. The military collector is more of a historian than other collectors.

There is a group of collectors who concentrate on HR steins, which are attributed to Hauber and Reuther of Freising, Bavaria, by Mike Wald in his book *HR Steins*. Theresa Thomas, in her book *Keramik*, attributes HR steins to Herman Roch. Collectors value HRs because they are limited in number, and usually marked, and are of high quality in some cases, particularly in their etched designs. The HR collector is convinced that his steins approach Mettlach quality, and it is interesting to hear arguments on both sides. I will not show my prejudices, but will admit that I own both types and will let the open market determine the price and quality of each.

Collectors also have an interest in occupational steins in which the scene on the body of the vessel depicts the occupation of the owner. This is a fascinating speciality with opportunities for acquiring rare pieces. There are many nice pottery, porcelain, and glass occupational steins, but it appears that they are becoming more difficult to obtain.

25

Particular subjects interest some collectors; there are sports, towers, Munich Child, miniatures, early glass, characters, Westerwald, Meissen, and etched steins. The list is infinite and collectors everywhere have different tastes and likes.

Some collectors are interested in obtaining particular series of steins, such as the Mettlach book steins of the 2001 series, which depict twelve professions, or the occupational series of Mettlach steins 2719 to 2730. This approach must surely be a challenge, and establishing a complete set must be gratifying. One collector recently purchased a stein from me to add to a set that had begun with the master three-liter stein.

I attended a stein auction recently and noticed a gentleman reading a newspaper as if completely uninterested in the proceedings. The sale contained a variety of steins with prices varying from $19 to $2,600 for a beautiful ivory stein with mythological figures. Finally, a faience stein appeared. The gentleman bid diligently and succeeded in beating his competition. He immediately folded his paper, paid his bill, and left the auction. His interest in this particular type of stein is another example of specializing. There are also numerous collectors searching for early Westerwald and Kreussen steins.

I know of one collector interested in tower steins. There are beautiful examples available in the market today, and the prices are still reasonable. At an auction last year, a group of collectors bidding on steins decided to allow a gentleman to purchase a nice two-liter old German tower stein and hence restricted the bidding. He was fortunate to obtain the piece for one hundred dollars. A collector called me a while back to say that he had just bought a beautiful three-liter tower stein and discovered that he may have a unique piece of pottery since this size is quite rare. The stein would be of value to the tower collector, but unfortunately its price may prohibit some from adding it to their collection.

Lithophane steins are attractive to many stein hobbists. Since the making of lithophanes is a specialty, most stein factories purchased them and did not produce them. I have found it a pleasure to show noncollectors the lithophanes on my steins, for these designs are often appreciated more than the steins themselves. It should be mentioned that specializing in a particular type of theme can lead to interest in creating a club. Clubs have been formed in the areas of lithophane, military, and Munich Child steins. The *Münchner Kindl* (Munich Child) is a symbol of Munich and Bavaria.

It can be difficult to complete a particular series or add to one's specialty. I have been searching for three years for a one-liter, blue-onion-pattern porcelain lithophane stein. Correspondence has led me to a collector who saw one in California many years ago. Assuming this information is correct, I will continue to search so that I can own three sizes.

Sports were popular in Germany and Europe in the nineteenth century, and certain collectors find this theme fascinating. Many bowling steins are available on the market today, and they range from etched scenes to characters.

Since collectors are always concerned with price and appreciation of investment, some are purchasing only etched steins. The makers and scenes are not as important as the quality of the etching. It is also easier to sell this type of stein as opposed to a relief or PUG (print under glaze). I own a beautiful one-liter etched stein with a matching ceramic insert lid that is of high quality. Unfortunately, the stein is unmarked, but I will keep it simply for the quality of the craftsmanship reflected in the pottery. This type of stein is often available at reasonable prices because unmarked pieces are passed over by many collectors.

The comedy theme, particularly as handled by the German artist Heinrich Schlitt, is popular today among Mettlach collectors. Collectors find the PUG scenes of Mettlachs quite humorous with dwarfs bowling, drinking, playing, or just sitting in nests. Scenes of drinking, running, or fighting in battle are also interesting, and collectors have purchased such steins for this reason. One collector revealed to me that fifteen years ago he was collecting only steins with dwarf scenes when he decided to diversify because he was becoming too specialized. He purchased a one-liter ivory stein to add to his collection two years ago. This is the way collectors' philosophies evolve.

Many collectors are interested in character steins, and since Dr. Eugene Manusov's *Encyclopedia of Character Steins* was published, interest in these steins has grown even more. I find them fascinating and amusing and have frequently shown some of mine to collectors and noncollectors. The opinions vary from "Isn't it cute?" to "What a nice face" and "Isn't it ugly?" Those who collect character steins must take the insults along with the praise.

The most desirable character steins are the Musterschutz porcelain ones, usually of animals, people and vegetables, although there are other types. The diligent collector appreciates the detail and mold work. The porcelain is delicate and lightweight, and it appeals to the eye. Some of the finest lithophanes are found in character steins, such as the "Nürnberg Funnel" and "LAW [League of American Wheelers] bicycle" steins. The character-stein enthusiast must be wary of reproductions as the market appears to be vulnerable. In fact, I viewed some outstanding reproductions being produced at the Rastel factory in Germany. They are well made and expensive, but they do not demand the price of an old Musterschutz.

One cannot force another collector to love or enjoy a particular type of stein. Art grows on an individual, and the true collector appreciates the philosophies of others. We purchase steins for our own gratification and cannot expect others to have similar tastes.

I do not specialize in any particular type of stein, but I do have a philosophy. I would like to build a collection of the best examples of the various makers who produced steins. To coincide with this approach, I hope to add excellent examples of all types of steins to my collection. In the near future, I will search for a Mettlach cameo stein because this will be a fine example of a stein produced by Villeroy and Boch at the turn of the century. As I purchase, I also consider the salability of the piece, recognizing that, as my interests change, I may wish to sell the stein and purchase others.

4

Purchasing Steins

Experience is the most valuable guideline when purchasing steins. All of us have learned through experience, and some of us have been "burned," as they say in the antique business. Unfortunately, a neophyte in the stein market will make mistakes. The hope is that he'll learn from them.

The most important criterion in evaluating a stein should be its aesthetic appearance. No one wishes to display a stein that is not attractive. Many characteristics make a stein appealing. The shape of the body is important. In the half-liter and one-liter steins, I prefer a body that is slightly tapered, sitting on a hollow base. Others prefer steins made with bulbous bodies. The pedestal base is appealing, particularly in certain glass and pewter steins. Usually, the body shape does not directly affect the price of the stein, but certainly one would not want to invest a large sum and be unhappy with the shape of the stein.

The most important characteristic determining price in pottery steins is whether the body is etched (engraved), done in relief, printed under glaze, or tapestry. The most desirable and expensive steins are the etched ones. Common pottery etched steins now command prices of over one hundred dollars in the half-liter size, and common etched Mettlach steins hover around five hundred dollars, with certain hard-to-find ones rising to two thousand dollars. Sophisticated collectors are now avoiding the purchase of pottery steins unless they are etched.

In purchasing a relief stein, look for detail in the relief. The finest relief steins have proportioned figures with intricate details that make them look real. Look for detail, intricacies, and price accordingly. A few Mettlach relief steins in the half-liter size are valued at over three hundred dollars because they meet these specifications. Relief steins that are less well executed are much cheaper.

Stein display.

Stein display.

The market is inundated with PUG steins. It's important that you shop for scenes that are attractive, just as you would if you were purchasing a painting for your living room. Since so many PUG steins are available, try to find a colorful scene that is noticed as soon as one looks at the stein. If the scene is exceptional, the price will be higher. Some PUG unmarked steins sell for as little as thirty-five dollars, and some expensive PUG Mettlachs approach three hundred dollars.

Since incised steins are so popular, it is worth mentioning that one should look for depth in the etching. The earlier steins made from a mold have greater depth than later ones from the same mold. When purchasing a stein, pay an appropriate price depending on the quality of the etching. One collector explained to me that he always runs his fingernails across the engravings to see if the etch is deep enough to produce a "corrugated" feeling.

Tapestry steins, except for Mettlachs, are rarely available. They are usually in the price range between relief and etched steins simply because the tapestry attached is usually etched, but the rest of the body of the stein is plain, thus placing the value of the stein lower than that of an etched Mettlach. I should mention that HR made excellent tapestry steins, and there are probably tapestry steins by other companies, although I haven't personally examined any. I have always felt that if the Mettlach artisans had added designs to the rest of the body of these steins, they would be highly attractive, and in some cases their prices would be higher than those of regular etched Mettlach steins.

Another factor that influences price is the thumblift. Someone should publish a guide on thumblifts, with appropriate photographs. By themselves, thumblifts do not greatly influence prices, but they do enhance the overall value of certain steins. Certain thumblifts are, at the least, attractive—the monkey, owl, jester, lyre, bust of figure, twin towers, eagle, Munich Maid, lion and shield, dwarf, and huntsman, for example—and they add to the overall appeal of the stein. I would advise an individual to pay a higher price for a stein if the thumblift is unique and authentic. I kept a stein for many years simply because of its twin-towers thumblift, coordinated with the pewter lid, which I felt placed the price at $125 instead of $75.

Lids are interesting, and they have a direct affect on the prices of steins. Many ceramic lids, particularly the etched ones, are nicely done. Examples of exceptional lids in ceramic are found on Mettlachs 1161, 1786, 1797, 2082, 2083, 2382, 2580, 2652, 2765, 2828, 2894, and 2917.

Collectors now search for ceramic lids, which place a higher value on a stein than pewter ones, particularly among Mettlach and Marzi and Remy steins. Originally, pewter lids were more expensive than ceramic ones, but not so today. Collectors fear replaced lids, and the market has numerous steins of this sort. Consequently, when the ceramic lid matches the stein body, collectors feel more secure. This may be the most important reason that a ceramic lid places a higher value on a stein than a pewter lid.

In purchasing military steins, it is crucial that the lid match the theme and branch of the military. Many neophytes have been fooled by military steins, and a particular kind of expertise is required in purchasing them.

Lids are important to glass steins, and the ones with the porcelain insert lids are especially attractive. Collectors display these steins by placing the open stein on a shelf upside down, allowing the lid to hang over the edge for display. Exceptional hand-painted porcelain lids raise values on plain glass steins up to one hundred dollars. Porcelain lids, then, are an added feature to clear glass steins whether they be pressed, etched, or cut. Many clear glass steins are purchased for their lids. In other glass steins, the color may be aesthetically attractive, and the lid becomes a secondary consideration.

Pewter lids, particularly the steeple (cone-shaped) ones with designs on them, can be attractive. Many flat lids have nicely etched or relief designs that are not normally noticed unless the stein is examined closely. Sometimes the finials have a figure or insert, and this adds to the quality of the lid since more workmanship was required. Military steins often have exceptional finials, and those with screw-off tops are particularly difficult to find. Since the face of the character stein, the most attractive part of the stein, is displayed on the lid, the lid is of the utmost importance in determining price. Beginning collectors should be cautious when purchasing character steins, although the opportunity to purchase one is rare. Many reproductions of character steins appear on the market, and some of them are of excellent quality and may appear to be old. It's safer to purchase only character steins that are clearly marked unless one is knowledgeable. Ordinary pottery characters are readily available, but the porcelain character steins are scarce and carry higher prices, especially those with the Musterschutz mark, which range from $250 to as high as $1,500 for a half-liter size. Rarity and workmanship are the two most important characteristics commanding high prices.

The presence of a lithophane can add to the value of a stein. To determine whether a porcelain stein has a lithophane, open the lid and look through the stein into the bottom. Be sure you have a bright light for a background. The lithophane is, in fact, a picture "hidden" in the base of the stein and can be viewed only from the inside. It is made by varying the thickness in the porcelain. If the porcelain is too thick, this will, of course, affect the translucency, and the picture will lack clarity. The more detailed and clear the lithophane is, the higher the value. Also look for unusual scenes, but be wary of nudes: the early stein makers did not produce them. Most lithophanes are in black and white, but colored ones do exist. Obviously, because of their scarcity, they are desirable and more expensive.

In general, steins with lithophanes are not uncommon, so be discriminating when purchasing them. Remember that it was common practice for people to drop items like keys or coins into their steins for safekeeping. Obviously, this would cause damage to the lithophanes at the bottom. Inspect the lithophane carefully for hairline cracks or other imperfections.

There are many other factors to consider when placing a price on a stein. Look for exceptional color on the body of the stein. Many colors faded during the day as workers painted, and the best colors were applied during the morning hours. Many steins have lost their true colors by being exposed to the sun over the years. There are significant differences in colors among Mettlach etched steins having the same mold number. The true, brighter colors are certainly more desirable, and color affects the final price. If possible, seek advice from colleagues on the true colors when making a high investment in a stein. Another collector may have a good example, and if you can compare your potential purchase, you should do so before you make a decision.

The open market determines the availability of a stein, and this in turn affects price. It is almost impossible to obtain a Royal Vienna stein at an auction or antique show. It is necessary to locate a collector who is willing to give one up. Another example is the Mettlach "Knight on a White Horse" (2765), every collector's dream. This stein, in the half-liter size, has been pushed to over $2,000. In my search for a one-liter onion-pattern porcelain stein, I have, without success, placed ads everywhere in national magazines for the past three years. Many of us have had to do this, and usually we pay the price when the stein we are searching for finally appears. Other steins difficult to locate are certain Musterschutz ones (Uncle Sam, Gentleman Rabbit) and Meissen, early Kreussen, and Capo-di-monte steins. Scarcity is certainly a determining factor, and collectors should be knowledgeable in case a particular stein appears and the opportunity to purchase arises. Those less knowledgeable may miss the opportunity for an excellent purchase.

Signatures appear on many steins, and this adds to the value just as signed paintings command higher prices. The name of the artist who designed the scene seems to identify the stein and to remove some of the element of the unknown. A Mettlach collector may be proud of the fact that a stein was designed by Heinrich Schlitt, Christian Warth, J. Stahl, or Fritz Quidenus. Actually, few steins are engraved with the artist's name. I do, however, have an HR 406 that is signed by Breindl and a pottery occupational (beer maker) signed by Maier.

Steins stamped with the factory mark usually command higher prices. There seems to be a kind of paranoia that prevents top-quality steins from selling for high prices if the maker is unknown. Steins that are stamped by Mettlach, HR, Merkelbach and Wick, Marzi and Remy, Reinhold Merkelbach, Thewalt, Gerz, and others will always be popular because the buyer is able to identify and date them. As noted earlier, when the factory stamp is omitted, the patent marks *gesetzlich geschützt, DRGM,* and *Musterschutz* identify the stein as pre-1920. These inscriptions plus "Germany" guarantee the stein's age and origin.

The beginning collector should be aware that all factories produced steins that run the gamut in quality. Do not pay a high price for a stein just because it was made by a particular company or because it is stamped and identified. Be discriminating in your purchase and look for all the other characteristics discussed in this chapter. Steins marked "Germany" could also be post–World War II, although most are pre–World War II.

When purchasing Mettlach steins, use *Villeroy and Boch 1885/Mettlach 1905,* published by Hans J. Ammelounx, to locate the original prices of the steins. (See the Bibliography for the English translation by Anton Post.) Manufacturers priced their steins according to the craftsmanship required to make them, and the informed collector should avail himself of this information. Although steins that are selling for high prices today were usually the most expensive when they first appeared on the market, there are numerous exceptions. Cameo steins are expensive today but were average in price when first produced.

The overall condition of a stein is important. Most collectors avoid repaired steins and only make exceptions on occasion. Minor defects include loose lids, loose tang attachment to pewter lid, loose straps, small cracks in the shank, some discoloration, slight overglazes, and stains. Broken shanks, replaced lids, cracks, noticeable hairlines, and broken handles count as major defects. The buyer must make some difficult decisions at times, but the general rule is to avoid steins with major defects and to use discretion on price if the stein is not perfect. This topic is open to debate, but I feel uncomfortable with defective or repaired steins. I have a few because I enjoy them, but it is extremely difficult to sell imperfect steins.

The age of a stein is important and, obviously, the older the stein, the greater the chance that it is not perfect. Steins produced before 1850 are difficult to locate. Most collectors have steins made between 1880 and 1920. Some collectors are willing to pay a higher price simply because a stein is older. One of my early steins is stoneware, circa 1860. It is not perfect, but I keep it because it has some nice features and because it is my earliest. I am not fortunate enough to have an early faience, Kreussen, or glass stein, but it is advisable to invest in at least one early desirable stein to add to the diversity of your collection. However, be prepared to spend many dollars as supply and demand push prices up.

Many collectors feel that stein prices have skyrocketed. This may or may not be true, but the prices of antiques in general, and particularly those of high-quality antiques, are climbing rapidly. I do not feel that steins are expensive when compared to similar objets d'art in the antique world. It is true that dealers have asked high prices for mediocre steins. I refuse to pay these prices and refrain from making purchases until the price is right. For the beginning collector, my advice is to assemble a small collection of high-quality steins and continually add to it. You may formulate a purchasing schedule based on the investment you can make. I take a percentage of my income and use it for purchasing steins. In fact, I have payroll deductions placed in a separate account in my credit union. This allows me to keep peace with my wife and organize my purchases.

5

Where to Buy Steins

Steins are becoming difficult to locate. Unless a collector actively seeks them, they rarely turn up. The purpose of this chapter is to encourage collectors to become active and thus increase their opportunities to add steins to their collections.

Many of us interested in antiques have attended auctions. In fact, my first stein purchase was at an auction. My wife and I had intended to purchase other items, but we noticed three steins for sale that looked interesting and decided to take a chance. I still own one of them, an etched half-liter for which I paid forty-five dollars. I found out years later that it was an unmarked HR stein.

Prices at an auction are usually lower than retail, but there are exceptions. Reasonable prices are more likely to be found at auctions where only one or a few steins will be sold. If many are for sale, collectors are more willing to travel long distances to attend. Few collectors will drive over an hour to an auction for one or two steins unless they are exceptional or ones they desire for their collections.

There are newspapers and antique magazines that advertise auctions and the serious collector should get this information on a weekly basis. The *Antique Trader* and the *Newtown Bee*, both distributed nationally, are examples of such publications.

It is advisable to arrive at the auction early so that the steins can be examined in detail. I have seen many individuals purchase steins with defects because they didn't study them before the sale and the auctioneer did not describe the damage. In some cases, the steins can be returned during the auction if a defect is noticed, but this can be embarrassing and it disrupts the auction.

Usually, if the steins are on one table together, everyone hovers over them, and you must work your way into the crowd. It's best to take your time and examine each stein, not just the ones that look interesting at first glance; there may be others that are "sleepers." You may find an unmarked stein that can be attributed to a particular company that others won't recognize. I usually have my wife attend with me because she has a better eye and can advise me of defects that I miss. Often a stein colleague is present, and I will ask him to examine a particular stein for me. Always ask your colleague first if he is interested in that particular stein; otherwise you ethically cannot solicit his opinion.

You may want to linger near the table after you have looked at the steins and listen for interesting comments that may or may not be helpful. Be cautious of individuals who "knock" a piece; they may be attempting to eliminate competition during the bidding. This is certainly an unethical practice, but it is used at auctions. There are other times when fellow collectors point out defects to each other during the preview.

It is wise to have the price you will pay set in your mind before the bidding begins. I have seen too many individuals get caught in the emotional atmosphere of the auction. There are competitors who don't quit until they get the final bid. You can find yourself paying well over retail price because you didn't set your price initially. Many years ago I saw a half-liter HR stein sell for $285 at a country auction. The retail value then was about $175, and the high price was the result of competitive bidding between two collectors.

When there are many steins available at an auction, I usually plan to allow someone else to purchase the Mettlachs unless the price is ridiculously low. I try to identify other steins whose quality people may not recognize because of the overwhelming interest in the Mettlachs. Also, these other steins usually come up for bidding early in the auction, before the Mettlachs, while everyone is cautiously waiting. If one waits until the end of the auction, when just a few steins remain, the selling prices are likely to be too high because collectors who have not yet purchased any steins feel they must go home with at least one.

It is difficult to assess the audience at an auction, but it's important that you get the feel of the crowd. Many times there are bidders who are not collectors. They recognize that prices for steins are high, but they do not discriminate in their purchasing. They bid high on common steins and may pay fifty or sixty dollars for steins that are available elsewhere for thirty-five or forty.

In the past, I would become excited and my blood pressure would rise prior to leaving for an auction. I'd plan to purchase one or more steins, but I don't recommend this approach to anyone. When I attend an auction now, I usually am open about purchasing. If I make a purchase, then I am happy with it, but if I don't, I am not disappointed. With competition increasing at auctions, there is a greater chance that one will not be able to make a purchase since there are many more interested individuals than available steins.

It is possible to enjoy an auction without bidding or buying. Some individuals record the prices and keep records for future reference. Attending auction previews and taking the opportunity to handle and examine the steins is a good learning experience. The bidding should also be observed as a learning experience to help you make appropriate decisions at future auctions. It is important to know whether steins are being sold on consignment or whether they come from an estate. I feel more comfortable if they are from an estate.

Many auctions include steins that are repaired or damaged. Be wary of repaired steins, especially at auctions. This is a good way to sell for someone who wants to dispose of pieces without having to face the buyer. Many auctioneers have to deal with this problem because consigners of steins are sometimes dishonest. If auctioneers buy steins outright, the purchaser at an auction still has to be alert because the auctioneer occasionally gets stuck with damaged and repaired pieces. Many collectors know they can fool an auctioneer with a repaired stein.

Often, collectors will get together at an auction to decide who is interested in certain steins and allow everyone involved to purchase without competition from other collectors. The goal, of course, is to keep the price down and limit the bidding to a single collector and the general audience. I have participated in this approach and have seen colleagues purchase excellent steins for low prices. It is difficult to create a group before an auction, but if only three or four collectors appear, it is possible to convene and make appropriate decisions. You may have to compromise and refrain from bidding on your first choice, but you may get another stein at a good price.

Some think that this conspiracy is unethical, but it isn't. Dealers have created pools for years, and auctioneers recognize this and live with it. By creating a pool, dealers have one representative bid on items they select. Instead of competing with each other and raising the prices, they have one person buy for the group (pool). Following the auction, the pool conducts its own auction and each member has a chance to bid on all purchases. All financial arrangements have been determined by the pool before the original auction.

Stein collectors, then, have three choices at an auction: (1) bid against each other; (2) create a group and allow each collector to bid on a stein he has selected; (3) create a pool and have a representative bid on all the steins the group selects.

If it is not possible to attend the auction, you still may be able to purchase steins. Some auctioneers accept absentee bids, which may be made during the preview or over the telephone. A representative of the auctioneering company will execute your bid and normally will enter the bidding after it has begun. It's quite possible to own the steins for less than your "left" bid. You cannot pay more than your bid except for a state tax or buyer's premium, which is usually 10 percent of the selling price paid to the auctioneer.

Leaving telephone bids for steins is a gamble because you are relying on the auctioneer for an accurate, honest description. It is wise to do business only with reputable companies. I have purchased some excellent steins this way, including some Musterschutz characters and Mettlachs, and have generally had good luck. However, I did have to reject a 2.4-liter etched Mettlach recently after noticing that the handle had been repaired. It had been described over the telephone as perfect.

If the auctioneer demands a down payment prior to the auction, be sure to include a statement that the bid be executed only if the stein is perfect or as described by the auctioneer over the telephone. I do not advocate purchasing steins in this manner. It is an uncomfortable feeling to pick up a stein that is not in the condition described. You can become involved in an argument and an unpleasant situation.

Sometimes there are auctions in which only steins are sold. I enjoy these auctions and usually find that the prices are reasonable because there are enough steins for everyone attending. Once again, though, the steins should be examined carefully because such auctions are good places to dispose of damaged and repaired pieces.

Steins can also be purchased at flea markets and antique shows. Antique dealers have many opportunities to purchase steins and enjoy selling them at their booths. Some dealers specialize and try to have steins at all their shows. Collectors who are willing to arrive at a show before it opens and wait in line may have the opportunity to purchase steins at reasonable prices.

It is everyone's dream to find a Mettlach at a flea market for $20, but unfortunately the days of "stealing" steins at shows are behind us. In fact, most dealers are overpricing their steins because they have heard that steins are in demand and are expensive. It is frustrating to see a common pottery relief stein for sale with a price tag of $125 or a common etched Mettlach for $575. It is best to ignore such steins and not comment, because they probably will not sell at those prices and the dealer will eventually realize that his prices are too high.

At a show, it's best to look for rare or unusual steins that may be priced too low. I recently purchased a one-liter stoneware stein with two defects for twenty-four dollars. I liked the stein, knew it was early (circa 1850), and, for the price, did not worry about the defects.

A collector should subscribe to antique magazines because they advertise steins for sale throughout the country. The same guidelines apply when purchasing by this route. You do not know the reputation of the seller, so it's important that you establish an agreement that the stein can be returned if you are not satisfied with it. Normally, a seller will allow someone three days to examine the stein and return it if not happy with it. This is fair to both parties, and I recommend that if a seller is not willing to agree to the return privilege the stein should not be purchased. It is best to telephone the party if you are interested in a stein. The call can be expensive, but you could lose the stein if you write a letter. I usually call and try to negotiate on the phone if there is a stein I really want to own. Collectors have to invest in calls, postage, and gasoline to purchase steins, but we don't include these expenses in our investment. Such expenses mean that some of my steins really cost 5 or 10 percent more than the price I paid for them.

Many steins are bought, sold, and exchanged through organizations of collectors. There are a number of stein collectors' regional clubs throughout the United States. All are affiliated with the national organization Stein Collectors International. The meetings are social in nature, and food and drinks are generally served. Usually, a guest lecturer is invited to discuss some topic related to steins. There are opportunities to purchase steins from fellow collectors at the meetings. Sometimes an exchange is possible. Many collectors would rather have a stein than the money to purchase one because it's difficult to find the ones they want for their collections.

There are advantages to purchasing a stein from a collector at a meeting. There is an unwritten code of ethics that prohibits one's colleague from selling you a damaged or repaired stein without making you aware of the repair. Also, you have other collectors available to react to quality and price before you make your decision. Having this experience available allows you to feel secure about a decision, and you will not get "burned," as you might purchasing from someone you don't know.

Collectors may also purchase steins through *Prosit,* the publication of Stein Collectors International (SCI). Collectors and dealers can advertise steins in the journal. Stein auctions are also advertised with or without pictures of steins. Prospective buyers mail their bids to the seller, and usually there is a minimum bid designated for each stein. The buyer who sends in the highest bid equal to or over the minimum is the successful owner of the stein. In most cases, the seller is accurate in his description. However, honest mistakes are made and are usually corrected between the two parties. I have purchased steins through SCI and have never had a problem. Again, all rules for purchasing should be followed by a collector. I recommend that collectors join SCI. *Prosit,* which is published quarterly, is excellent and provides invaluable information. SCI itself is a highly professional organization. Dues are twenty dollars a year. The mailing address is P. O. Box 463, Kingston, New Jersey 08528.

Collectors can try to locate steins in their area by inserting advertisements in the local newspapers. I have had limited success with this approach, but I intend to keep trying. Be prepared to go on wild-goose chases. Many times the descriptions on the telephone are incomplete, and it's best to visit the person to view the stein. However, it's advisable not to allow individuals to visit you; you will be letting a stranger into your home who could be surveying your collection and other valuables for possible theft. When you begin to insert ads in the newspapers, you also expose yourself as a collector of objets d'art. This is a decision each individual has to make; maintaining anonymity is important to most people. Also, there are individuals who simply want their steins appraised. Try to discover if they are serious about selling; otherwise you provide an appraisal service at no cost.

It is also possible to advertise nationally in magazines such as the *Antique Trader.* Usually someone responds and the fee is a good investment. It's important to develop communications with collectors and dealers who do respond. I have established a card and letter file for reference and use it periodically. Make a list of where steins are available and the names of individuals who have offered certain steins for sale. You may not buy initially, but you could change your mind in the future.

Many collectors will not buy a stein unless the price is a bargain. It is not always possible to get a bargain, and I suggest that you pay retail price for a stein you desire for your collection. This past year I paid retail price for a ruby red stein at an antique show. I had reserved a special place on my favorite table for the stein, and I decided that I had looked long enough. I am pleased that I made the decision.

6

Where to Sell Steins

At one time or another, most collectors are in the position of having to sell a stein from their collection. The purchase of an expensive stein often necessitates selling another to finance it. Collectors commonly upgrade their collections in this manner, although most of us regret having to part with an item from our collection.

There are numerous ways to sell steins, but collectors are mistaken if they plan to make great profits on ordinary steins unless they were purchased cheaply and kept for a number of years. I have been quite pleased if I could make a fifteen-dollar profit on a stein I purchased for thirty-five dollars and owned for two years, particularly if there wasn't any overhead.

Steins of high quality are usually easy to sell if one knows the best avenues. It's possible to minimize overhead, sell directly except for mailing costs, and make a nice profit. Much has been written these past few years about antiques as an investment. It appears that a 10 percent profit on a high-quality stein one year after purchase is reasonable. Some will argue that this figure is too small, but individuals who seek greater profits are responsible for pushing up the costs of steins. The basic assumption in applying the 10 percent figure is that the stein was originally purchased at the open market value. Obviously, there is greater profit if one purchases steins below market value. If a higher price was paid for a stein, the collector should wait for the price to catch up before he tries to sell.

Collectors can often sell steins to antique dealers, although most dealers want only Mettlach steins. Be prepared for an insult; the dealer may offer you 50 percent less than the value you place on your steins, particularly the common ones. Keep in mind that the dealer is in business to make a profit. Many collectors sometimes forget this. When one purchases a stein from a dealer at a fair price, it is because the dealer purchased it for a price less than market value.

On high-quality steins, such as Mettlach, Musterschutz character, and Royal Vienna steins, a dealer is sure that he can sell the stein quickly. Hence, he may offer a price only 10 or 20 percent less than market value, and the collector may be able to make a fair profit, particularly if he has owned the stein a number of years. I know of one dealer who will pay $400 for a Mettlach stein because she knows she can sell it for $475 or $500 without having to advertise it. This is a good profit for her, and the collector also does well.

The best way to locate a dealer who purchases steins is to call a local dealer and ask if he is aware of any colleagues who purchase steins. Most dealers know the specialties of their colleagues. It is best to search for a dealer who purchases steins regularly; since he has a market, he can probably offer you more.

A collector can advertise in antique magazines such as the *Antique Trader*. The cost is about eight or ten dollars for a small ad. It's important to select an appropriate magazine that reaches the potential market. I have attempted to sell steins through an antique magazine that specializes in Early American furniture and primitives. Since most subscribers to this journal are not interested in steins, the responses to my ads have been limited. I suggest that photos be made available upon request, especially of steins that are difficult to identify from the description in the ad. Include in your overhead the cost of your photos, phone calls, and mailing fees. Also, the price offered is usually less than the asking price, so prepare for this as you write your ad and determine your prices. If you have many steins for sale, it's a good idea to include a photo with descriptions in the ad so that potential buyers can make an immediate decision. This type of ad is expensive, but you may sell more steins.

It's important to be fair to the buyer by allowing him to return the stein within a three- to five-day period if he is not satisfied with it. Most people who purchase steins through ads know that pictures and descriptions can sometimes make a stein appear to be of high quality when it isn't. You will be more likely to sell a stein if you advertise that it may be returned if the buyer is not satisfied.

To avoid having steins returned, be honest and accurate in your descriptions. Don't overlook minor defects, such as loose lids, stains, or small hairlines. Some collectors are perfectionists and will not own steins with minor defects. It is best to describe defects as in the following example:

> MERKELBACH AND WICK POTTERY—
> ½ L etched stein, tavern
> scene, very good except hair-
> line on rim of body, $80.

In this description, you have indicated the maker, which is important. The size and type (etched, pottery) are also mentioned, as is the scene. The one defect is included along with the price. Your opinion of the condition (very good) is inserted, and this places the stein in a particular category as opposed to excellent, mint, or perfect. It's not necessary to say much else, particularly if a picture is shown or available on request.

Auctions are places to buy steins, not to sell them. Some will disagree, but I have seen too many excellent steins purchased cheaply at auctions and, of course, have had the opportunity to purchase some for my collection. There are exceptions, and steins have sold too high in some instances, but undervaluing seems to be more prevalent.

I had the experience recently of consigning four glass steins to an auctioneer in New Hampshire. Over a three-year period, I had paid $200 total for the four pieces. I was hopeful that the four steins would sell for $300, so after the 20 percent commission I stood to make $40 profit. I did not attend the auction and do not know the circumstances under which my steins were sold, but I received a check in the mail two weeks following the auction for $72. The steins had sold for $90 minus 20 percent commission. Just prior to this auction, I had bought for $350 an etched Mettlach that was valued between $500 and $600, which offset my loss on the sale of the glass steins, but I still have not recovered from this unpleasant experience.

In general auctioneers sell steins for whatever price bidders are willing to pay. High-quality steins such as Mettlachs usually sell for market value at auction, but the 20 percent commission leaves the owner with an amount far less than if he had sold it himself. Some auctioneers are now charging a 10 percent commission to the consigner and 10 percent to the purchaser. You should review the options and plans of a number of auctioneers before making a decision.

An auction may be a good place to sell steins with defects. You must be honest with the auctioneer and point out the defects. However, after this is done, your ethical obligations have ended. Some auctioneers will obtain an excellent price for your defective steins, and you do not have any obligations to the customers, who may or may not be aware of the deficiencies.

An auction may also be a good place to sell your cheaper steins, because there will be many noncollectors there who may pay high prices for them. I have seen common twenty-five-dollar steins sell for forty dollars at auctions.

A collector should try to identify the stein market. It takes years to accomplish this. Some collectors accumulate lists of individuals and the steins they want. They turn to these lists when they have a particular stein to sell.

The best stein market can be reached through Stein Collectors International. I have had success buying and selling through *Prosit*, and the meetings of SCI's local chapters offer opportunities to sell steins. Collectors are usually reasonable with their prices when selling to each other. It is best to adopt this approach and to be sure to point out any defects to an interested colleague. You cannot afford to damage your reputation with members of your local chapter.

7

Price Guide

Since the purpose of this book is to assist the beginning collector, I feel that the prices listed here for the various steins will be of practical value in helping the newcomer buy and sell. Establishing accurate prices has been quite a feat. I have discussed the pros and cons of including prices in the book with many collectors. Some fear that the prices will inflate the market and that collectors will have less opportunity to purchase steins at a reasonable cost. I feel that the prices may help correct dealers and auctioneers who are asking too much for their steins. The open market has always allowed prices on antiques and collectibles to increase or decrease, and published price guides have had little inflationary effect.

An investment philosophy that is prevalent today advocates the purchase of antiques as a hedge against inflation. Assuming the stein market draws more interest in the future, prices will increase accordingly, just as they have for Early American furniture, oriental rugs, paintings, oriental porcelain, and other antiques and collectibles.

Prices on all steins other than the Mettlachs and characters were obtained by consulting with collectors. I have kept a history of prices for the past three years, and I used this as a reference also. Since I attend antique shows and auctions regularly, I feel that my records provided me with accurate guidelines. When there was little or no information available, I choose not to price the steins. I intend to be accurate and fair to everyone and wish not to mislead those collectors using the book.

In pricing the Mettlach and character steins, I conducted a nationwide survey and asked collectors and dealers to respond to the prices I had researched. The survey form was difficult to prepare because the aim was to ascertain accurate prices on nearly three hundred steins, but the response was excellent. The returns were over 60 percent, with respondents representing twelve states and all the major regions of the country.

The survey offered respondents choices on each stein. They could agree with the price I assigned, disagree and insert their own, or leave it blank if they were not familiar with the stein. I found that in some cases collectors made the latter decision rather than guess the value of a stein. This was appreciated.

I decided not to average the results because the high and low prices on some steins were extremely divergent. Instead, I tried to find a price that was common and that represented most of the individuals who responded. For a majority of the steins, prices were remarkably close, and it was not difficult to assess a representative figure. On some steins, the prices were too far apart and I decided to avoid taking a guess. For example, I had one Mettlach priced at $550, and the responses ranged from a low of $500 to a high of $1,200. Since there was no agreement, I decided to list no price for this stein.

The prices given are for steins in mint condition, and any duplicate stein in less than mint condition will obviously be worth less. The prices are intended to be guidelines, and one should always consider a range when purchasing or selling. If one were to choose a percentage for the variation, it would appear that on the more expensive steins, such as etched Mettlachs or Musterschutz characters, a range of 5 percent is reasonable. On less expensive steins, a range of 5 or 10 percent can be expected.

As an example, I cite the popular St. Florian Mettlach 1786 in the half-liter size priced at $750. Using the 5 percent guideline, the range of this stein is a low of $712.50 to a high of $787.50. Any purchase price less than the former is a good buy; a price over the latter may be too high. Keep in mind that there are many reasons for paying a particular price for a stein and that in some cases the guideline may be ignored.

Finally, it should be noted that the prices for the survey were established in 1980 but were revised and updated in March 1981 for this volume.

Pewter Steins

1. Size: ½ *l.* Description: Relief decoration on body, pedestal base, face on thumblift. Price: $135.

2. Size: ½ *l.* Description: Floral design on plain body. Price: $85.

4. Size: 1½ *l.* Description: Relief, mythological figures, dated 1914, names inscribed at top of body, excellent lid and relief work. Price: $325.

3. Size: ½ *l.* Description: Relief, hunters, woman, dogs, deer, and bird. Price: $185.

5. Size: ¼ *l.* Description: Plain body, alligator handle, lid dated 1905, glass base. Price: $75.

7. Size: ½ l. Description: Etched, three men at table, lid dated 1912. Price: $225.

6. Size: 1 l.Description: Tankard, possibly English, early nineteenth century. Price: $250.

8. Size: 1 l. Description: Etched, two men at table. Price: $275.

9. Size: 1 l. Description: 1979 SCI convention stein, limited edition. Price: $115.

Glass Steins

10. Size: ¼ l. Description: Ruby flashed, three panels with etched building in each, stone insert on thumblift. Price: $150.

11. Size: ³⁄₁₀ l. Description: Ruby flashed, etching of viaduct on body. Price: $140.

13. Size: ¼ l. Description: Ruby flashed with bird. Price: $125.

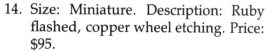

12. Size: ½ l. Description: Ruby flashed, pewter lid. Price: $135.

14. Size: Miniature. Description: Ruby flashed, copper wheel etching. Price: $95.

15. Size: ½ *l.* Description: Ruby flashed, pressed pattern on body. Price: $135.

16. Size: ½ *l.* Description: Ruby glass with etched building, ornate pewter lid. Price: $165.

17. Size ½ *l.* Description: Painted deer, glass insert lid. Price: $100.

18. Size: ½ *l.* Description: Hand-painted horses and dogs. Price: $110.

21. Size: ½ l. Glass with handpainted flowers, nice pewter lid. Price: $100.

19. Size: Miniature. Description: Swedish stein, blue molded glass. Price: $95.

20. Size: ½ l. Description: Amber opalescent glass with flowers, ornate pewter lid of sculling scene, boy on dolphin thumblift. Price: $175.

22 Size: 1½ l. Description: Amber color with cavalier, exceptional handle. Price $235.

23. Size: 3 *l.* Description: Yellow color with painted floral decoration. Price: $250.

24. Size: 1 *l.* Description: Biedermeier, pedestal base, dated 1848 on pewter lid, floral design. Price: $300.

25. Size: 1 *l.* Description: Yellow glass with hand-painting (red eagle and shield). Lid is Viking helmet with ram thumblift. Price: $265.

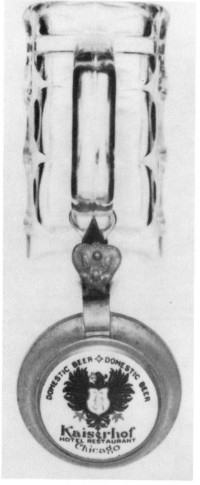

26. Size: ½ *l.* Description: Thumbprint glass with porcelain insert lid, marked *Chicago, Kaiserhof Hotel Restaurant.* Price: $65.

50

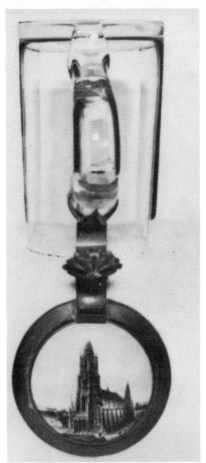

27. Size: ½ *l*. Description: Clear glass with porcelain insert lid—church. Price: $70.

28. Size: ½ *l*. Description: Clear glass with inverted thumbprint pattern on body, handpainted porcelain insert of lady on lid. Price: $95.

29. Size: ½ *l*. Description: Amber color, thumbprint with pewter base. Price: $150.

30. Size: ½ *l*. Description: Amber color with pedestal base. Price: $160.

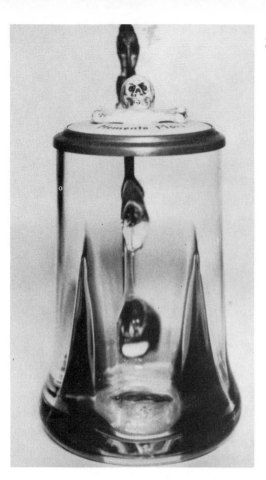

31. Size: ½ *l*. Description: Clear glass with green pattern, Stevens & William of England are makers, but skull and bones lid are German; made for S.S. soldier, as indicated under lid. Price: $300.

33. Size: ½ *l*. Description: Plain clear ribbed glass with glass overlay on gold. Price: $125.

32. Size: 1 *l*. Description: Amber glass with ornate pewter overlay, lion thumblift. Price: $275.

34. Size: ½ *l*. Description: Cobalt blue color with pewter bird thumblift. Price: $150.

35. Size: ½ *l*. Description: Etched deer in body, lid has glass insert, pedestal base. Price: $210.

36. Size: ½ *l*. Description: Glass stein has nice porcelain insert lid—Heidelberg, eagle thumblift. Price: $150.

37. Size: ¼ *l*. Description: Eagle painted on white glass. Price: $105.

Miscellaneous Steins

38. Size: 1½ *l.* Description: Pewter overlay on wood. Price: $250.

39. Size: 1 *l.* Description: Tusk with brass lid and handle, brass foreleg of horse for handle and spur thumblift. Price: One of a kind, but probably expensive.

Pottery Steins

40. Size: ½ l. Description: PUG, man and woman dancing on hillside with people in background, marked *Merkelbach & Wick* with *R* under base, two engraved lions on pewter lid. Price: $120.

42. Size: 1 *l.* Description: PUG, floral decoration, early *Merkelbach & Wick* mark under base and 1341. Price: $175.

41. Size: ½ *l.* Description: Etched, two dwarfs, one sitting on a mushroom, marked *Merkelbach & ·Wick* under base. Price: $150.

43. Size: ½ *l*. Description: Relief, four panels with many figures in each, copy of Kreussen, *Merkelbach & Wick* mark under base. Price: $125.

45. Size: ½ *l*. Description: PUG, monk painting, some hand-painting on body, *Merkelbach & Wick* mark under base, exceptional pewter lid engraved with twin towers thumblift. Price: $135.

46. Size: ½ *l*. Description: PUG, lion, marked *Merkelbach & Wick* under base, engraved pewter lid. Price: $75.

44. Size: ³⁄₁₀ *l*. Description: PUG, cavalier holding stein, *Merkelbach & Wick* mark under hollow base. Price: $95.

47. Size: ½ l. Description: Etched, frog smoking a pipe, marked *Merkelbach & Wick* and *1171* under base. Price: $165.

48. Size: ½ l. Description: Etched, two men and woman at table on patio. *Thewalt* mark under hollow base along with *Musterschutz, Germany,* and *425*. Price: $165.

49. Size: ½ l. Description: Etched; one stein has bowling scene while other has scene of man and woman. Both have mermaid handle, marked *Musterschutz* along with *Thewalt* mark (circa 1900). Price: $150 each.

50. Size: 2 *l.* Description: Relief, figures in many colors, Viking lid, signed *GK* on body. Price: $200.

51. Size: 1 *l.* Description: Relief, man dancing and two women watching, signed *KB* on body. Price: $135.

52. Size: 2½ *l.* Description: Relief, hunter blowing bugle; lid is hunter sitting with dog. Marked *187* under base, signed *KB* on body. Price: $200.

53. Size: ½ *l.* Description: Relief, gentleman with goblet, signed *KB* on body, country girl lid. Price: $125.

58

54. Size: 2 *l*. Description: Relief, gentleman in forest, signed *KB* on body, marked *1127* under base, lid is man sitting playing instrument, woman and dog. Price: $225.

55. Size: 3 *l*. Description: Relief, Siegfried and dragon, dragon handle, signed *KB* on body, marked *1264* under base, detachable lid of Viking and maid. Price: $250.

56. Size: ½ *l*. Description: Etched, Thirsty Rider, *Marzi & Remy*. Price: $200.

57. Size: 1 *l*. Description: Etched, two elves drinking in tree with two owls, owl in ceramic lid, marked *O* under hollow base, *Marzi & Remy*. Price: $325.

58. Size: Miniature. Description: Relief, designs, marked *252* under base. Price: $25.

59. Size: Miniature. Description: Relief, green color with designs, no markings. Price: $25.

60. Size: Miniature. Description: Relief, blue salt glaze, marked *A6* under base. Price: $35.

61. Size: Miniature. Description: Relief, St. Louis stein, marked *Germany* under base. Price: $30.

62. Size: Miniature. Description: Relief, six miniature steins and one slightly larger on tray. Price: $175 (complete set).

63. Size: 1 *l*. Description: Octagonal body with blue designs, marked *gesetzlich geschützt* under base and under pewter lid. Price: $150.

64. Size: ¼ *l*. Description: Blue lines around stoneware body, no markings. Price: $45.

65. Size: ½ *l*. Description: Occupational, fireman, blue salt glaze, three panels, marked *RH–Germany* under base. Price: $110.

66. Size: ¼ *l*. Description: Relief, blue salt glaze, cavalier with woman, marked *Germany* under base, two other panels on body. Price: $60.

67. Size: 1 *l*. Description: Relief, blue salt glaze, lovers sitting on a bench, marked *Germany* under base. Price: $100.

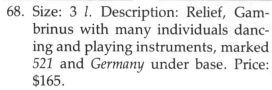

68. Size: 3 *l.* Description: Relief, Gambrinus with many individuals dancing and playing instruments, marked *521* and *Germany* under base. Price: $165.

69. Size: 5 *l.* Description: Relief, man and two women, signed *GK* on body, marked *100 Germany O* under base, *Girmscheid*. Price: $300.

70. Size: ½ *l.* Description: Relief, blue salt glaze, three panels in which two have designs and third has soldiers, marked *RM* and *232* under base. Price: $85.

71. Size: ½ *l.* Description: Relief, six cherubs, no markings. Price: $50.

72. Size: ½ l. Description: Relief, two men and two women at table, cream color against blue background, no markings. Price: $55.

73. Size: 1 l. Description: Relief, drinking scene, no markings. Price: $85.

74. Size: 1½ l. Description: Relief, five panels with a figure in each, marked *Germany 702* under base. Price: $125.

75. Size: ½ l. Description: Relief, three panels to include a cavalier in one, woman in a second, and a man and woman in third. Price: $75.

76. Size: 1 *l.* Description: Relief, three panels, a man and woman dancing in one and cupid in each of other two, music box under base, heavy stein. Price: $110.
77. Size: 1 *l.* Description: Relief, hunting scenes. Price: $100.
78. Size: 1 *l.* Description: Relief, two men and woman and another man pouring beer into instrument, marked *67—0* under base, very heavy stein. Price: $100.
79. Size: 1 *l.* Description: Relief, early stoneware with three panels, Gambrinus in center panel, porcelain insert lid. Price: $135.

80. Size: 2 *l*. Description 1978 SCI convention stein, white stoneware with gold bands, figures of the old monastery in Mettlach, designed by Jo van Zundert of Villeroy & Boch Co. Price: $125 at time of issue.

81. Size: 2 *l*. Description: PUG, blue gray stein with ram's head under pouring spout, no markings. Price: $125.

82. Size: ½ *l*. Description: PUG, gentleman, no marks. Price: $50.

83. Size: ½ l. Description: PUG, mountain scene with man and woman. Price: $75.

84. Size: ½ l. Description: PUG, Munich Maid, pewter lid has knights in relief and Munich Maid thumblift, no markings. Price: $95.

85. Size: 1 l. Description: PUG with some hand-painting, figures in mountain lake scene, hollow base, nice pewter lid and thumblift, very colorful. Price: $150.

86. Size: ½ l. Description: PUG, man drinking, no markings. Price: $50.

1½ *l.* amber glass stein.

1 *l.* PUG pottery stein with floral decoration.

2 *l.* pottery stein done in relief.

Steins on a mantelpiece.

Mettlach occupational steins.

1 *l.* etched pottery stein.

1 *l.* pottery stein with octagonal body.

1 *l.* PUG pottery stein.

½ *l.* amber glass stein with pedestal base.

Florida stein.

½ *l.* pottery stein, beer maker occupational.

½ *l.* pottery stein done in relief.

½ *l.* porcelain stein, furniture maker occupational.

½ *l.* etched stein, HR 406.

½ *l.* etched stein, HR 420.

½ *l.* etched stein, HR 1002.

½ *l.* etched stein, HR 413.

½ *l.* relief stein, HR 453.

½ *l.* etched stein, 1551 (believed to HR).

½ *l.* relief stein, HR 452.

½ *l.* etched stein, HR 421.

½ *l.* etched stein, HR 476.

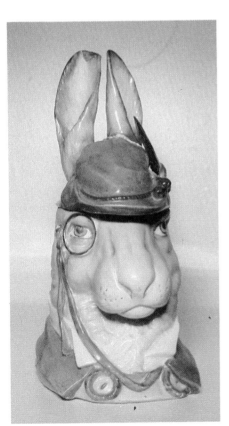

½ *l.* character stein: "Gentleman Rabbit."

1 *l.* relief stein, HR 454.

1 *l.* character stein: Frauenkirche tower.

½ *l.* character stein: tower with Munich Maid.

1 *l.* character stein: Munich Child.

½ *l.* character stein: Munich Chil

½ *l.* character stein: fat cat.

½ *l.* character stein: wraparound alligator.

1½ *l.* character stein: "Lavender Lady."

½ *l.* character stein: marksman.

1 *l.* etched stein, Mettlach 1786: "Saint Florian with Dragon Handle."

½ *l.* character stein: Munich Child.

½ *l.* character stein: student.

½ l. character stein: wealthy gentleman.

½ l. character stein: monk.

½ l. character stein: rhinoceros

½ l. mosaic stein, Mettlach 1192.

½ l. etched stein, Mettlach 1162: "Peasant Dance."

½ l. etched stein, Mettlach 1520: "National Coats of Arms."

½ l. etched stein, Mettlach 1566.

87. Size: 6 *l*. Description: PUG with hand-painting, three panels with a man drinking in each, marked *Germany E* under base, *Prosit* stein, very colorful. Price: $400.

88. Size: ½ *l*. Description: PUG, Munich Maid, no markings, twin tower thumblift. Price: $75.

89. Size: ½ *l*. Description: PUG, cavalier, marked *338—A* under base, nice pewter lid. Price: $85.

90. Size: 3 *l*. Description: PUG, tavern scene with some hand-painting, marked *1180* under base, stein is Christmas gift, lid dated 1894. Price: $275.

91. Size: ½ *l.* Description: Occupational, beer maker, Gambrinus, and scenes of brewery, owner's name. Pewter lid has monk in relief and monk thumblift, signed *Maier* under base. Price: $250.

92. Size: 1 *l.* Description: Etched, man bowling surrounded by wreath, ceramic lid of pins and ball, marked *1087* under base. Price: $185.

93. Size: 1 *l.* Description: Etched, man talking with two women, marked *1333* under base. Price: $150.

94. Size: 1½ *l.* Description: Etched, tavern scene, marked *1339* under base. Price: $195.

95. Size: ½ *l.* Description: Etched, six figures drinking, marked *RM* and *447* under base, nice pewter lid. Price: $150.

96. Size: ½ *l.* Description: Etched, three men arm in arm, marked *Girmscheid Co.* Price: $135.

97. Size: 2½ *l.* Description: Etched, three men drinking at a table and woman standing, marked *1359* and *Germany* under base. Price: $225.

98. Size: ½ *l.* Description: etched, tavern scene, marked *1720* under base. Price: $110.

99. Size: ¼ l. Description: Etched, various designs on body, marked *110* under base. Price: $50.

100. Size: 3 l. Description: Etched, scene of man and woman eating and drinking and marked *1390* under base. Price: $200.

101. Size: ³⁄₁₀ l. Description: Etched, wine cellar scene with taster and barrels of wine in background, marked *1295* under base. Price: $75.

102. Size: ½ l. Description: Etched, four men watching man and woman dancing, marked *Germany 1554* under hollow base. Price: $125.

103. Size: ½ *l.* Description: Etched, two men sitting at table and woman seated near window, ceramic lid, marked *Germany 1334* under base. Price: $100.

104. Size: ½ *l.* Description: Relief, black boy with banjo and alligator, also alligator handle, marked *Germany 6042—11* under hollow base. Price: $125.

105. Size: ½, ¼, ⅛ *l.* Prices: $125, $75, $50.

106. Size: ½ *l.* Description: Etched, souvenir of Florida stein with alligator handle, marked *Germany 6044* under base. Price: $235.

107. Size: ½ *l.* Description: Relief, souvenir of Florida stein with alligator handle, marked *6049* under base. Price: $125.

107a. Florida steins.

108. Size: ½ *l.* Description: Military stein, Infantry, 2nd Co. 4th Infantry, Prince Wilhelm No. 112 Mulhausen, 1909–11, Baden. Price: $350.

109. Size: ½ *l.* Description: Military stein, Infantry Bodyguard Regt. Grand Duchess (3 Grand Duke Hesse) No. 117—Mainz, 1902–04. Price: $285.

110. Size: ½ l. Description: Military stein, Field Arty. Regt. von Holtzendorf (l Rheinish) No. 8—Saarbrücken and Saarlouis, lithophane of soldier and maiden, removable artillery shell, 1904–06. Price: $350.

111. Size: 1 l. Description: Military stein, Infantry Regt. von Goeben (2 Rheinish) No. 28—Ehrenbreitstein 1910, marked *744* under base. Price: $400.

Porcelain Steins

112. Size: ½ l. Description: Traveler with dog talking with lady in window, lithophane of man on horse. Lid has dried flowers under glass prism. Price: $275.

113. Size: ½ l. Description: Tavern scene, lithophane of castle. Lid has dried flowers under glass prism. Price: $275.

114. Size: ½ *l.* Description: Writing on body with limited designs, lithophane of Wilhelm I. Price: $110.

115. Size: ½ *l.* Description: Shepherd talking with woman, lithophane of man and woman sitting on a bench. Price: $160.

116. Size: ½ *l.* Description: City scene, lithophane of man and woman dancing, pedestal base. Price: $125.

117. Size: ¼ *l.* Description: Man and woman, lithophane of two men and women at table, pedestal base. Price: $95.

118. Size: ½ *l.* Description: Man and woman, nice pewter lid, lithophane of monk in wine cellar, very heavy stein. Price: $200.

119. Size: ½ *l.* Description: Pictures and designs on body give impression of family crest, etc.; unusual thumblift. Lithophane of hunters leaving tavern, signed *W. Wild.* Price: $200.

120. Size: ½ *l.* Description: Tavern scene, hunters and woman, lithophane of hunters saying good-bye, pedestal base. Price: $150.

121. Size: ½ *l.* Description: Souvenir stein, lithophane of hunter saying good-bye to two men, pedestal base. Price: $125.

122. Size: ¼ *l.* Description: Hunter on mountain side, exceptional lithophane of woman sitting and couple walking. Price: $95.

123. Sizes: ½, ¼ *l.* Description: Blue onion pattern, lithophane in ½ *l.* of embracing couple and in ¼ *l.* of man and woman on mountain side. Prices: ½ *l.*, $250; ¼ *l.*, $150.

124. Size: ½ *l.* Description: Floral design. Price: $100.

125. Size: ¼ *l.* Description: Two soldiers with a barmaid, marked *Hanke— Germany* under base. Price: $95.

126. Size: ½ *l.* Description: Four men bowling and pin boy. Price: $125.

127. Size: ½ l. Description: Indian on each size of body, marked *Manning Bowman and Co., Meriden, Conn.* under base. Price: $75.

128. Size: ½ l. Description: Occupational, possibly road repairman, lithophane of man and woman in house. Price: $200.

129. Size: ³⁄₁₀ l. Description: Occupational, farmer, lithophane of two women. Price: $185.

130. Size: ½ l. Description: Occupational, furniture maker. Lithophane of man and woman inside house, owner's name. Price: $225.

131. Size: ½ l. Description: Delft, windmill and lake with sailboat; insert lid
has windmill. Price: $210.
132. Size: 1 l. Description: Delft, blue
color with windmill. Price: $275.
133. Size: 2 l. Description: Soldier,
marked *Royal Bonn Delft* under base.
Price: $500.
134. Size: ½ l. Description: A distin-
guished gentleman, marked *Royal
Bonn Delft* under base, circa 1880.
Price: $250.

135. Size: 1 *l*. Description: Faience, early, Russian Imperial Eagle with flowers on each side. Price: $1200 to $1500.

136. Size: 1 *l*. Description: Faience (later), horse and leaves, pewter base. Price: $250.

137. Size: ½ *l*. Description: Military stein, Field Artillery, 2 Lorraine Field Arty. Regt. No. 34, Metz, lithophane. Price: $300.

138. Size: ½ *l.* Description: Military stein, Infantry, 13th Bavarian Inf. Regt. 1912–14, face on handle, screw-off top, lithophane of soldier saying farewell. Price: $375.

139. Size: ½ *l.* Description: Military stein, cavalry, 5th Regt. Albrecht, 1896–99, lithophane of woman and man in kitchen. Price: $300.

140. Size: ½ *l.* Description: Military stein, artillery, 4 Battery 4 Field Artillery Regiment, Augsburg, 1908–10, lithophane of farewell scene. Price: $350.

14l. Size: ½ *l.* Description: Military stein, Infantry, 3 Inf. Regt. Prinz Carl Von Bazern, 7 Comp. Augsburg 1910–12, removable top shows company and battle scenes. Lithophane of man and woman in farewell scene. Owner is Lance Corporal Ambros Schmid. Price: $350.

142. Size: ½ *l.* Description: Military stein, Infantry, 2nd Infantry Regiment, 4th Co. Munich, lithophane of King Ludwig, pictures of K. Wilhelm and Prince Leopold on body, owner's name on base. Price: $300.

143 Size: ½ *l.* Description: Military stein, Infantry, 10 Infantry Company Kaiser Wilhelm at Ulm. 1904–06, prism top of campfire scene on insert, lithophane of man holding hand of lady in farewell scene. Owner's name on body. Price: $300.

HR Steins

144. Size: ⁴⁄₁₀ *l.* Description: Mosaic, *139,* green and blue designs. Price: $115.

145. Size: ½ *l.* Description: Etched, *154,* red coloring, musicians, dancers and drinkers. Price: $200.

146. Size: ½ l. Description: Tapestry, *156*, Munich Child, *M. Willman—Berlin*, engraved under lid. Price: $185.

147. Size: ½ l. Description: Etched, *160*, tavern scene with musicians, card playing. Price: $210.

148. Size: ¼ l. Description: Etched and relief, *237*, designs. Price: $95.

149. Size: ½ l. Description: Salt glaze, *239*. Price: $100.

150. Size: ½ l. Description: Etched, *406*, wedding scene, signed *Breindl*. Price: $275.

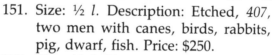

151. Size: ½ l. Description: Etched, 407, two men with canes, birds, rabbits, pig, dwarf, fish. Price: $250.

152. Size: ½ l. Description: Etched, 413, six figures, beer party, woman holding steins and waiting. Price: $240.

153. Size: ½ l. Description: Etched, 419, six dwarfs and four frogs having a party. Price: $240.

154. Size: ½ l. Description: Etched, 420, three men and dog, lamplighters. Price: $285.

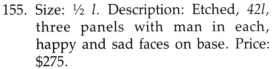

155. Size: ½ l. Description: Etched, 421, three panels with man in each, happy and sad faces on base. Price: $275.

156. Size: ½ l. Description: Etched, 445, four men, monkey sitting on cat and holding fish. Price: $275.

157. Size: ½ l. Description: Etched, 446, rowboat scene, seven figures. Price: $250.

158. Size: ½ l. Description: Relief, *452*, man playing fiddle, couple sitting and couple dancing, white figures against beige background. Price: $185.

159. Size: ½ l. Description: Relief, *453*, boy, three men walking, woman on porch. Price: $185.

160. Size: 1 l. Description: Relief (color), *454*, man at table, couple hugging, man and woman. Price: $260.

161. Size: 1 *l.* Description: Relief, *456*, garden scene, four figures, nice pewter lid, etched writing on body. Price: $275.

162. Size: ½ *l.* Description: Relief, *457*, seven military figures including a drummer, white figures on blue background. Price: $175.

163. Size: ½ *l.* Description: Etched, *476*, five musicians. Price: $235.

164. Size: ³⁄₁₀ *l.* Description: Etched, *501*, couple sitting and holding hands, couple with dog on other side. Price: $210.

165. Size: 1 *l*. Description: Etched, *541*, tavern scene. Price: $350.

166. Size: ½ *l*. Description: Etched, *1002*, tennis scene, floral designs on sides. Price: $285.

167. Size: 1 *l*. Description: Relief, *1925*, wedding scene, thirteen figures. Author believes this is HR though mark not under base. Price: $250 (assuming stein is HR).

168. Size: ½ *l*. Description: Etched, *1551*, six figures. Author believes this is HR though mark not under base. Price: $225 (assuming stein is HR).

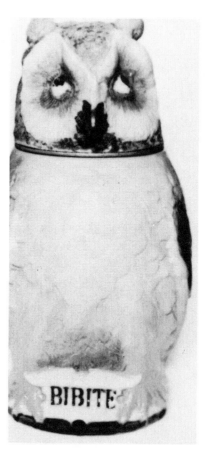

169. Size: ½ *l.* Description: Barrel, pottery, Mettlach *675.* Price: $200.
170. Size: ½ *l.* Description: Owl, pottery, Mettlach *2036.* Price: $950.
171. Size: ½ *l.* Description: Pretzel, Mettlach *2388.* Price: $425.

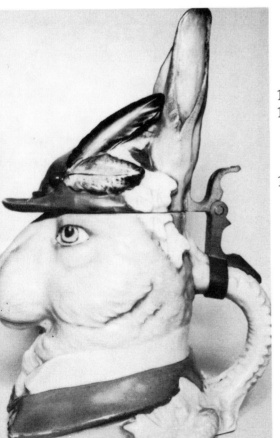

172a. Size: ½ *l*. Description: "Gentleman Rabbit," porcelain, green Tyrolean hat with dark brown feather, beige face with gold monocle on right eye, green collar, *Musterschutz* and hash mark under base. Price: $1,250.

172b. Same as 172a.

173. Size: 3 *l*. Description: "Sad Radish," porcelain, marked *Musterschutz* under base. Price: Rare stein, expensive.

174. Size: ½ *l*. Description: Drunken monkey, porcelain, beige color, marked *Musterschutz* with hash mark under base. Price: $500.

175. Size: ½ l. Description: Elf, porcelain, beige, marked *Musterschutz* with hash mark. Price: $900.

176. Size: ½ l. Description: Uncle Sam, porcelain, deep beige, marked *Musterschutz* with hash mark. Price: $1350.

177. Size: ½ l. Description: Cat with hangover, porcelain, beige color, marked *Musterschutz*. Price: $500.

178. Size: ½ l. Description: L.A.W. bicycle (League of American Wheelers), porcelain, lithophane, marked *Musterschutz*. Price: $350.

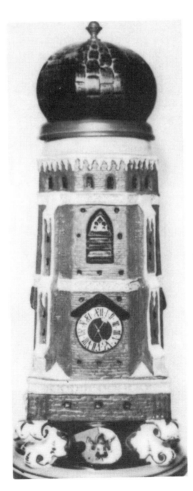

179. Size: ½ l. Description: Singing pig, porcelain, marked *Musterschutz* under base. Price: $400.

180. Size: ½ l. Description: Hops lady, porcelain, marked *Musterschutz* with hash mark under base. Price: $525.

181. Size: ½ l. Description: Tower, pottery, no markings. Price: $200.

182. Size: ½ l. Description: Tower, pottery, beige and green color, marked *Germany* under base. Price: $175.

183. Size: 1 l. Description: Frauenkirche tower, porcelain, body is red, brown, and white, dome is green marked *Martin Pauson–München, gesetzlich geschützt N126* on body beneath handle, lithophane. Price: $1,250.

184. Size: ½ l. Description: Salzburg tower pottery, marked *gesetzlich geschützt* under base. Price: $225.

185. Size: ½ l. Description: Tower, pottery, Munich Maid on front, marked *1414* under base. Price: $275.

186. Size: One 3 l. and six ½ l. Description: Towers, pottery, matching set, marked *T. W. and gesetzlich geschützt* under base. Price: Set $1,800 ($200 for ½ l. and $600 for 3 l.).

187. Size: ½ l. Description: Skull, pottery (glaze), marked *gesetzlich geschützt—Germany 1796* under base. Price: $350.

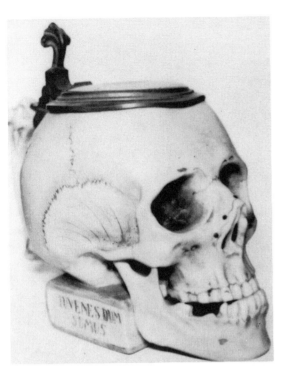

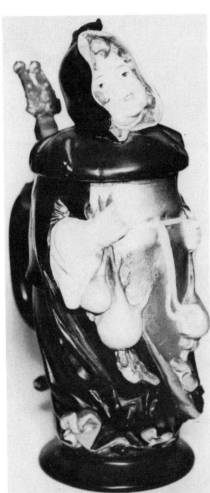

188. Size: ½ l. Description: Skull, bisque, marked *E. Bohme Soehne 9136/3* under base. Price: $400.

189. Size: ¼ l. Description: Munich Maid, pottery, marked *gesetzlich geschützt* under base. Price: $120.

190. Size: 1 l. Description: Munich Child, pottery with bisque head, marked *1285* under base. Price: $225.

191. Size: ½ l. Description: Munich Child, bisque, lithophane, signed by Joseph Mayer. Price: $600.

192. Size: ½ l. Description: Munich Child, pottery, marked *117;* other unknown mark under base. Price: $165.

193. Size: 1½ l. Description: "Lavender Lady," pottery, marked *gesetzlich geschützt 732* under base. Price: $450.

194. Size: ½ l. Description: "Mother-in-law," pottery, marked *geschützt 680* under base. Price: $195.

195. Size: ½ l. Description: Student, pottery, light brown and black colors. Price: $225.

196. Size: ½ l. Description: "Umbrella Man," pottery, marked *geschützt 738* under base. Price: $185.

197. Size: ½ l. Description: Marksman, pottery, *J. Reinemann München—gesetzlich geschützt* under base, dark brown body. Price: $200.

198. Size: ½ l. Description: Wealthy gentleman, pottery, marked *175* with Thewalt mark. Price: $250.

199. Size: ½ l. Description: Cavalier, pottery, marked *Germany 1439* under base. Price: $225.

200. Size: ½ l. Description: Monk, porcelain, brown body, black cap, lithophane of couple dancing. Price: $275.

201. Size: ½ l. Description: Black boy, porcelain, marked *geschützt F 737* under base. Price: $285.

202. Size: ¼ l. Description: Indian, bisque, lifelike face with nice overall colors. Price: $400.

203. Size: ½ l. Description: Beehive, pottery, bees appear on body, marked *1384* under base. Price: $225.

204. Size: ½ l. Description: Football, pottery, marked *Germany 6* under base. Price: $175.
205. Size: 1 l. Description: Bowling pins, pottery, no markings. Price: $235.
206. Size: ½ l. Description: Rhinoceros, pottery, marked *Germany 1451* under base, possibly Steinzeugwerke. Price: $295.
207. Size: ½ l. Description: Military frog, pottery, marked *27* under base. Price: $225.

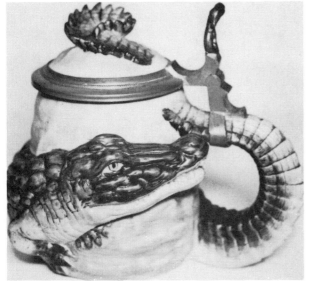

208. Size: ½ l. Description: Fat cat, pottery, marked *511* under base, beige, brown, and green color, green eyes. Price: $195.

209. Size: ½ l. Description: Owl, pottery, various shades of brown, marked *530* under base. Price: $195.

210. Size: ¼ l. Description: Ram, pottery, no markings. Price: $90.

211. Size: ½ l. Description: Wraparound Alligator, bisque, greenish alligator wrapped around body of stein, blue body representing water. Price: $650.

Mettlach Steins

212. Size: ½ *l.* Description: VB, early, relief, designs on body. Price: Too wide a range.

213. Size: ½ *l.* Description: VB, early (723 painted on lid) relief. Three men; one is peeking out of stein, another lying on ground, and third is next to stein. Price: Too wide a range.

214. Size: ½ *l.* Description: 202, relief. "Singers." Five people holding books and singing, writing etched into body on sides, white figures on blue background. Price: $310.

215. Size: ½ *l.* Description: VB 280, PUG. Gambrinus surrounded by eleven figures. Price: $200.

216. Size: ½ l. Description: 589, PUG. "Life at the Pub." Two men at table, one drinking, other smoking. Price: $185.
217. Size: ½ l. Description: 812, relief. "The Hunter." Three panels with hunting scenes, white figures against tan background. Price: $310.
218. Size: 1 l. Description: 1053, etched. "Gnomes." Three dwarfs drinking and having a good time. Price: $685.
219. Size: ½ l. Description: 1068, mosaic. Floral design on body. Price: $295.

220. Size: ½ l. Description: 1132, etched. "Musician on the Nile." Man playing fiddle, alligator and sphinx. Price: $550.

221. Size: ½ l. Description: 1146, etched. "Students." Seven students drinking, barmaid and dog, signed *Warth.* Price: $500.

222. Size: ½ l. 1154, etched. Description: "The Hunter." Four panels with hunting scenes. Price: $550.

223. Size: 1 l. Description: 1154, etched. "The Hunt." Four panels with hunter in each, leaves background, same stein as 1695 but leaves included. Price: $700.

224. Size: ½ l. Description: 1162, etched. "Peasant Dance." Three panels with couple dancing in each one; rare brass lid and thumblift. Price: $560. This price represents stein with ceramic lid—not brass, which raises the price because it is so rare.

225. Size: ½ l. Description: 1163, etched. "Village Musicians." Five musicians with leaves on body as background. Stein 1471 is same without leaves. Price: $550.

226. Size: ½ l. Description: 1164, etched. "Drinker." Five figures drinking. Price: $495.

227. Size: ½ l. Description: 1192, mosaic. Birds and designs. Price: $395.

228. Size: ½ *l.* Description: 1379, etched. "Architecture." Three panels with engineer in each. Price: $500.

229. Size: ½ *l.* Description: 1395, etched. "French Playing Cards." Four scenes, each with a different card. Price: $450.

230. Size: ½ *l.* Description: 1396, etched. Cherub drinking out of large stein, inlay lid has fish on plate and cat. Price: $495.

231. Size: ½ *l.* Description: 1397, etched. Man on front, designs on rest of body. Price: $460.

232. Size: ½ *l.* Description: 1403, etched. "Bowling." Bowling scene and drinking. Price: $495.

233. Size: ½ *l.* Description: 1453, etched. "Hunter." A hunter in front panel, two dogs and two boars. Price: $525.

234. Size: ½ *l.* Description: 1460, relief and etched. Head of horse in relief and designs. Price: $400.

235. Size: ½ *l.* Description: 1519, etched. Men in boat rowing in one panel and one man in boat in another panel. Price: $575.

236. Size: ½ *l.* Description: 1520, etched. "National Coats of Arms." Black eagle and two cavaliers. Price: $575.

237. Size: 1 *l.* Description: 1526, PUG. Cavalier blowing bugle. Price: $285.

238. Size: ½ *l.* 1526, PUG. Yale stein. Price: $195.

239. Size: 1 *l.* Description: 1526/702, PUG. Gambrinus and numerous other figures dancing. Price: $295.

240. Size: 3 *l.* Description: 1526/1038, PUG. Frogs swimming and drinking, keg next to water, signed *Heinrich Schlitt*. Price: $575.

241. Size: ½ *l.* Description: 1526/1101, PUG. Barmaid with steins. Price: $175.

242. Size: 1 *l.* Description: 1526/1109, PUG, "Wandering Musicians." Four figures in band. Price: $270.

243. Size: 1 *l*. Description: 1527, etched. "Old German Group of Drinkers." Drinking scene, signed *W*. Five figures total: one is playing instrument. Price: $695.

244. Size: ½ *l*. Description: 1530, PUG. Student smoking pipe. Price: $400.

245. Size: ¼ *l*. Description: 1539, mosaic, floral design. Price: $175.

246. Size: ½ *l*. Description: 1566, etched. Man on high-wheeled bicycle waving hat. Price: $625.

247. Size: 5 *l*. Description: 1577, etched. "Old German Dinner Scene." Twelve figures around body of stein, much detail. Price: $2,000.

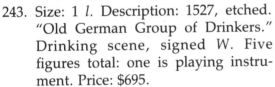

248. Size: 1 *l*. Description: 1641, tapestry. "Figure from the Lowlands." Gentleman smoking a pipe. Price: $385.

249. Size: 1 *l*. Description: 1642, tapestry. "Artist," drinking from beaker. Price: $385.

250. Size: ½ *l*. Description: 1643, tapestry. "Student", drinking from stein. Price: $275.

251. Size: 1 *l*. Description: 1647, tapestry. "Peasant." Man has scowl on face. Price: $385.

252. Size: ½ *l*. Description: 1655, etched. "Native Bavarian Dancers." Four dancers, designs on each side of handle. Price: $525.

253. Size: ½ l. Description: 1662, tapestry. "Smithies." Young blacksmith. Price: $285.
254. Size: ½ l. Description: 1675, etched. "Views of Heidelberg." Price: $500.
255. Size: ½ l. Description: 1695, etched. "Hunter." Four panels with a hunter in each. Price: $500.
256. Size: ½ l. Description: 1724, etched. "Fireman." Occupational stein. Price: $625.
257. Size: ¼ l. Description: 1725, etched. "Lovers—Old German Costumes." Cavalier holding stein up to his lady friend. Price: $350.

258. Size: ½ *l*. Description: 1733, etched. "Pictures of Jockeys." Three panels with jockey and horse in each. Jockey's cap on lid. Price: $800.

259. Size: 1 *l*. Description: 1786, etched. "Saint Florian with Dragon Handle." Saint Florian, the protector against fire and floods, is putting out a fire. Price: $950; ½ l., $750.

260. Size: ½ *l*. Description: 1795, etched. "Views of Freiburg." Town in mountain setting. Price: $500.

261. Size: ½ l. Description: 1796, etched. "Old German Drinker." Three panels: (a) Monkey and stein, (b) cavalier, and (c) cat. Price: $550.

262. Size: ½ l. Description: 1797, etched. "Assorted Figures." Four panels with a man in each; panels have each suit of cards. Gold coins on ceramic lid. Price: $625.

263. Size: ½ l. Description: 1823, etched. Hunter shooting gun, two dogs, bird, geese and rabbit in scene. Price: $525.

264. Size: ½ l. Description: 1856, etched. "Imperial Postal Eagle." Postman's stein. Price: $695.

265. Size: 1 l. Description: 1856, etched. "Imperial Postal Eagle." Same as ½ l. Price: $925.

266. Size: ½ *l*. Description: 1909/727, PUG. Dwarfs bowling. Price: $220.
267. Size: ½ *l*. Description: 1909/732, PUG. Three panels, a figure in each. Price: $220.
268. Size: ½ *l*. Description: 1909/1010, 1909/1009, PUG. "Gnome Bar" and "Gnomes Pressing Wine." Price: $195 each.
269. Size: ½ *l*. Description: 1909/1073, PUG. "Sunday Hunter, with Verse." Price: $195.
270. Size: ½ *l*. Description: 1909/1339, PUG. Fox playing violin, dwarf playing base, and rabbit blowing horn; also ducks. Price: $215.

271. Size: ½ l. Description: 1914, etched. "Athlete": a "4F" stein. The 4F or Turnverein Society was founded in Germany in 1811 by Friedrich Ludwig Jahn for people interested in mental and physical fitness. The four Fs stand for *frisch, fromm, froh,* and *free* ("fresh," "loyal," "happy," and "free"). Every five years certain cities held athletic events as an outgrowth of this society. Price: $650.

272. Size: ½ l. Description: 1915, etched. Buildings in city: signed *Warth*. This stein has different city views on front panel. Price: $565.

273. Size: ½ l. Description: 1932, etched. "Old German Drinkers." Two cavaliers toasting. Price: $550.

274. Size: ½ l. Description: 1934, etched. "Military Uniforms from 1689–1889." A soldier in each panel with a date. Price: $675.

275. Size: 3 l. Description: 1940, etched. "Cooper with Tankards, with Drinking Verse." Young man holding a stein; same scene as 1941. Price: $1,200.

276. Size: 3 l. Description: 1941, etched. Young man holding stein; same scene as 1940. Unusual body shape for this size. Price: $1,275.

277. Size: ½ l. Description: 1968, etched. Young lovers surrounded by flowers. Price: $525.

278. Size: ½ l. Description: 1972, etched. "Female Figures representing the Four Seasons." Four panels. Price: $550.

279. Size: ½ l. Description: 1997, etched. Picture of George Ehret, the brewer; designs on each side of body. Price: $450.

280. Size: ½ l. Description: 1998, etched. "Trumpeter from Sackingen." Price: $535.

281. Size: ½ l. Description: 2001A, glazed. "Book Backs for Lawyers." Titles of books on body represent the legal profession. Twelve steins for twelve different professions were made in this series. Price: $525.

282. Size: 1 l. Description: 2002, etched. "Munich with Beer Verse." Munich Maid with house of Munich as background. Price: $585; ½ l. $435.

283. Size: ½ l. Description: 2004, etched. Two foxes with common tail as handle, owl in front of body, stein most likely one for university students. Price: Too wide a range but likely to be expensive.

284. Size: ½ l. Description: 2007, etched. "Tomcat Hiddigeigei" from the opera *The Trumpeter from Sackingen*. This stein is in series along with 2008 and 2009. Signed *F. Stuck*. Price: $665.

285. Size: ½ l. Description: 2008, etched. "God Be with You." Trumpeter on horse, from the opera *The Trumpeter from Sackingen*. This stein is in series along with 2007 and 2009. Signed *F. Stuck*. Price: $610.

286. Size: ½ l. Description: 2009, etched. "Werner and Margarete," couple from the opera *The Trumpeter from Sackingen*. This stein is in series with 2007 and 2008. Signed *F. Stuck*. Price: $600.

287. Size: ½ l. Description: 2012, etched. "Hansa Symbols." Price: $500.

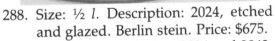

288. Size: ½ l. Description: 2024, etched and glazed. Berlin stein. Price: $675.

289. Size: ½ l. Description: 2024 and 3043, etched and glazed. Berlin and Munich steins. Prices: $675 and $1,000.

290. Size: ½ l. Description: 2025, etched. "Wild Carousing." Sixteen cherubs carrying someone. Price $465.

291. Size: 1 l. Description: 2027, etched. "Gambrinus." Gambrinus strolling, monkeys and owl. Price: $700.

292. Size: ½ l. Description: 2028, etched. "Drinker's Round." Party scene with eleven figures. Price: $550.

293. Size: 1 l. Description: 2028, etched. "Drinker's Round." Eleven figures in a drinking scene. Price: $695.

294. Size: ½ l. Description: 2029, etched. "Military Marksmanship." Two soldiers and target, girl. This stein is in series with 2030 and 2031. Price: $625.

295. Size: ½ l. Description: 2030, etched. "Soldiers and Tomcat." Three soldiers; one pouring beer from keg. This stein is in series with 2029 and 2031. Price: $650.

296. Size: ½ l. Description: 2031, etched. "Maneuver Joke." Three soldiers; one is on guard duty and is hiding girl in bushes during inspection. This is in series with 2029 and 2030. Price $650.

297. Size: ½ *l.* Description: 2035, etched. "Parade of Bacchus." Eight figures with god Bacchus. Price: $475.

298. Size: 4 *l.* Description: 2038, glazed. "Rodenstein Hamlets and Castle," usually referred to as the "Black Forest Stein," shows houses and trees in Gersprenz, Odenwald, and Beerfurth: green body. Price: $4,000.

299. Size: ½ *l.* Description: 2049, etched. "The Chess Stein." Price: Too wide a range but likely to be expensive.

300. Size: ½ *l.* Description: 2050, etched. "Slippers in Marriage." Young couple, slipper on lid. Price: $625.

117

301. Size: ½ *l*. Description: 2051, etched. "Student Feast." German university students in a tavern. Price: $650.

302. Size: ¼ *l*. Description: 2052, etched. "Munich Child." Possibly a baby gift since this was customary. Price: $435.

303. Size: 4 *l*. Description: 2053, glazed. 4F athletic stein, barbells, bears lifting weights and steins. See 1914 for information on 4F Society. Price: Too wide a range but likely to be expensive.

304. Size: ½ *l*. Description: 2054, etched. Tyrolean man raising stein, signed W. Price: $510.

305. Size: ½ *l*. Description: 2057, etched. "Peasant Dance." Seven figures dancing and holding steins, terra cotta red body. Price: $450.

306. Size: 2.4 *l.* Description: 2065, etched. "Councilor from the Lowland and Barmaid." Two figures, bird, fox and sun in background, signed *H. Schlitt.* Price: $1,250.

307. Size: ½ *l.* Description: 2074, etched. Blackbird in cage drinking from stein. Price: Too wide a range but likely to be expensive.

308. Size: ½ *l.* Description: 2075, etched. "Emblems of the Railroad." German Imperial Eagle; could be occupational stein for railroadman. Price: $675.

309. Size: ½ *l.* Description: 2082, etched. The William Tell stein. Tell shooting apple from son's head. Price: $1,100.

310. Size: ½ *l.* Description: 2083, etched. The Boar Hunt Stein. Price: $1,175.

311. Size: ³⁄₁₀ *l.* Description: 2082 and 2083. William Tell and boar hunt in smaller size. Prices: $850 and $925.

312. Size: ½ *l.* Description: 2089, etched. Angel giving stein to man having his dinner. Price: $565.

313. Size: ³⁄₁₀ *l.* Description: 2090, etched. Man seated at table with stein, cards, and dice, wife waiting with a broom. Price $450.

314. Size: ½ *l.* Description: #2091, etched. Saint Florian is pouring water over man who is drunk. Saint Florian is the protector against fire and floods. Price: $775.

315. Size: ½ l. Description: 2092, etched. Dwarf changing clock in presence of owl, signed *H. Schlitt*. Price $595.

316. Size: ½ l. Description: 2093, etched. Four panels, cards of all suits in each, very colorful. Price: $650.

317. Size: ½ l. Description: 2094, etched. Eight figures, band with lady playing fiddle, dancing. Price: $550.

318. Size: 2½ l. Description: 2095, etched. "Drinking Germans and Romans, with Verse." A statesman and soldier are viewing two Germans drinking from keg. Scene is humorous. Price: $1,400.

319. Size: ½ l. Description: 2097, etched. Music stein. Price: $500.

320. Size: ½ l. Description: 2100, etched.
Roman soldier drinking from stein
while man (German) dressed in robe
with club and horn speaks to him,
signed *H. Schlitt*. Price: $825.

321. Size: ½ l. Description: 2101, etched.
Woman serving pig's head on a plat-
ter while man is waiting, black color
in background. Price: $565.

322. Size: ⁴⁄₁₀ l. Description: 2106, glazed.
Cage forms of body of stein with
monkeys in cage, monkey handle.
Price: $675.

323. Size: 2.25 l. Description: 2107,
etched, "Gambrinus in His Empire."
Gambrinus on throne with barmaid,
signed *H. Schlitt*. Price: $1,350.

324. Size: ³⁄₁₀ l. Description: 2123, etched.
Knight in armor drinking from a
large stein, signed *H. Schlitt*. Price:
$595.

325. Size: ½ *l*. Description: 2130, cameo. Three panels with Gambrinus in center one. This stein may have been made in relief but one pictured is cameo. Price: $750.

326. Size: ½ *l*. Description: 2133, etched. Dwarf drinking in tree. Price: $925.

327. Size: ³⁄₁₀ *l*. Description: 2134, etched. "Drinking Gnomes." Dwarf sitting in nest with two steins. Price: $850.

328. Size: ½ *l*. Description: 2140, PUG. Man and woman on bicycle on one side, six young bicyclists on other side. Price: $275.

329. Size: ½ *l*. Description: 2140, PUG. Baseball scene on one side, rugby scene on other. Harvard stein. Price: $295.

330. Size: ½ *l*. Description: 2140, PUG. Baseball scene on one side, rugby scene on other. Princeton stein. Price: $295.

331. Size: ½ *l*. Description: 2140/941. "Inn with Beer Barometer." Four figures in scene highlighted by lady sitting under umbrella, meeting a customer holding up a pear. Price: $220.

332. Size: ½ l. Description: 2140/952, PUG. Man on bicycle on one side; boy, swans, and train on other side. Price: $300.

333. Size: ½ l. Description: 2140/1147. Scene with seven dwarfs. Price: $235.

334. Size: ½ *l.* Description: 2182, relief. "Peasants Bowling on Blue Background." Bowling scene with score-keeper and other man off to one side. Price: $325.

335. Size: ½ *l.* Description: 2184/967 (*left*) and 2184/966 (*right*), PUG. Humorous dwarf scenes on each stein, some relief work on each body, inlay ceramic lid: both belong to serving stein 2183/953. Price: $285 each.

336. Size: ½ *l.* Description: 2190, etched. Cyclists on one side and fairgrounds on the other; it appears they are congratulating the winner of the race; total of seven cyclists on body. Price: $675.

337. Size: ½ *l*. Description: 2192, etched. "Student Joke, Etruscan Style." Man with keg of beer in one panel, two students and dog heading for keg of beer in other panel, black background. Price: $750.

338. Size: 2.75 *l*. Description: 2193, etched. Five figures and a dog, black body. Price: $1,600.

339. Size: 1 *l*. Description: 2204, etched. "Imperial Eagle." Price: $885.

340. Size: 5.2 *l*. Description: 2205, etched. "Hunter and Diana, Drinking with Verse." Knights, ladies, hunter, dogs, and slain boar; pottery squirrel lid and pewter boar thumblift. Scene is party following the hunt. Price: $2,800.

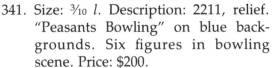

341. Size: ³/₁₀ *l.* Description: 2211, relief. "Peasants Bowling" on blue backgrounds. Six figures in bowling scene. Price: $200.

342. Size: ½ *l.* Description: 2230, etched. "Councilor from the Lowland and Barmaid." Gentleman holding stein to barmaid. Price: $565.

343. Size: ½ *l.* Description: 2231, etched. "Old German Soldiers." Four men drinking at table. Price: $560.

344. Size: ½ *l.* Description: 2235, etched. "Barmaids." Woman holding two mugs beside target. Price: $625.

345. Size: ½ *l.* Description: 2238, etched. National Guard stein, excellent colors. Price: Too wide a range but likely to be expensive.

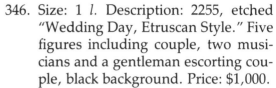

346. Size: 1 *l*. Description: 2255, etched "Wedding Day, Etruscan Style." Five figures including couple, two musicians and a gentleman escorting couple, black background. Price: $1,000.

347. Size: 2.25 *l*. Description: 2261/1012, PUG. "Old Germans at Drunken Feast." Two soldiers, child, wolf, signed *H. Schlitt*. Price: $550.

348. Size: ½ *l*. Description: 2271/981, PUG. "Rowing Regatta." A number of boats with crewmen, many people waving. Price: $250.

349. Size: ½ *l*. Description: 2271/1055, PUG. "Old German Drinker in Front of Barrel, with Verse." Two drunken cavaliers being observed by monkeys, which are laughing. Price: $250.

350. Size: ½ *l*. Description: 2276, etched. "Nuremberg Goose-Boy." Boy is in relief in panel, rest of body has etched designs. Price: $475.

351. Size: ½ l. Description: 2277, etched. "Nuremberg Castle." Price: $525.

352. Size: ½ l. Description: 2281, etched. New York National Guard stein, 23rd regiment, excellent colors. Price: Too wide a range but likely to be expensive.

353. Size: ½ l. Description: 2282, etched. "Beer Cellar Scene." Boy getting caught pouring beer from keg. Price: $575.

354. Size: ½ l. Description: 2288, etched. New York National Guard stein, 7th regiment, excellent colors. Price: Too wide a range but likely to be expensive.

½ l. character stein: military frog.

½ l. etched stein, Mettlach 1797: "Assorted Figures."

3 l. etched stein, Mettlach 1940: "Cooper with Tankards, with Drinking Verse."

1 l. etched stein, Mettlach 2027: "Gambrinus."

½ l. etched stein, Mettlach 2049: "The Chess Stein."

1 l. PUG stein, Mettlach 5019/5442.

½ l. etched stein, Mettlach 1154: "The Hunt."

4 l. glazed stein, Mettlach 2053: 4F athletic stein.

½ l. etched stein, Mettlach 2075: "Emblems of the Railroad."

2½ l. etched stein, Mettlach 2095: "Drinking Germans and Romans with Verse."

1 l. etched stein, Mettlach 2012: "Hansa Symbols."

½ l. etched and glazed stein, Mettlach 2024: Berlin stein.

½ l. etched stein, Mettlach 2051: "Student Feast."

½ l. etched stein, Mettlach 2100.

½ l. etched stein, Mettlach 2238: National Guard stein.

1 l. etched stein, Mettlach 2255: "Wedding Day, Etruscan Style."

1 *l.* Capo-di-monte stein.

½ *l.* etched stein, Mettlach 2583.

5½ *l.* etched stein, Mettlach 2300: "Figures from *Meistersinger*."

½ *l.* stein, Mettlach 2382: "The Thirsty Knight."

½ *l.* etched stein, Mettlach 2441: "Old German Drinkers Playing Dice."

½ *l.* etched stein, Mettlach 1655:
"Native Bavarian Dancers."

½ *l.* etched stein, Mettlach 1733:
"Pictures of Jockeys."

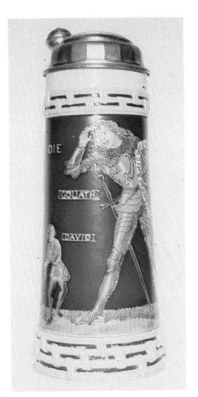

½ *l.* etched stein,
Mettlach 2635:
"Girl Bicyclist."

1.4 *l.* etched stein,
Mettlach 2682:
"Woman Vintner."

1 *l.* etched stein,
Mettlach 2718: "David and
Goliath, with Verse."

½ *l.* etched stein,
Mettlach 2767:
"Munich Child."

½ l. etched stein, Mettlach 2192:
"Student Joke, Etruscan style."

½ l. character stein: cavalier.

½ l. relief stein, Mettlach 2526: "Hunt
Scene, Kreussen Style."

½ l. cameo stein, Mettlach 2530:
"Hunt Scene."

½ l. etched stein, Mettlach 2004.

1 *l.* etched stein, Mettlach 2717: "Amor Cupid as Marksman, with Verse."

½ *l.* etched stein, Mettlach 2580: "Kannenburg."

½ *l.* etched relief stein, Metlach 2585: "Munich Child on Top of Globe."

l. etched stein, Mettlach 2765: Knight."

½ *l.* PUG stein, Mettlach 2789: "Drinker."

½ *l.* etched stein, Mettlach 2833D: "Not a Drop Left in the Stein."

½ *l.* glazed stein, Mettlach 2829: "Rodenstein."

½ *l.* etched stein, Mettlach 2190.

½ *l.* stein, Mettlach 5190/5015.

½ *l.* etched stein, Mettlach 2726: goldsmith occupational.

³⁄₁₀ *l.* etched stein, Mettlach 2833E: "I Had a Comrade."

355. Size: 5½ l. Description: 2300, etched. "Figures from *Meistersinger*." Four panels on main body with a man in three panels and a woman in fourth. In fifth panel, at top, is a rooftop view of Nuremberg. Price: $2,750.

356. Size: ½ l. Description: 2302, etched. "Children Playing Music, Etruscan Style." Eight children forming band, each playing an instrument. Price: $600.

357. Size: ½ l. Description: 2324, etched. Old-time football game. Price: $675.

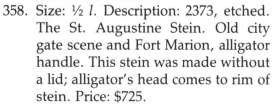

358. Size: ½ *l*. Description: 2373, etched. The St. Augustine Stein. Old city gate scene and Fort Marion, alligator handle. This stein was made without a lid; alligator's head comes to rim of stein. Price: $725.

359. Size: ½ and 1 *l*. Description: 2382. "The Thirsty Knight." Knight pouring beer from keg, signed *H. Schlitt*. Price: ½ *l*., $720; 1 *l*., $1,000.

360. Size: 1 *l*. Description: 2391, etched. "Wedding March of the Swan Knight." Seven figures in wedding scene. Price: $2,000.

361. Size: ½ *l*. Description: 2394, etched. "Three scenes from Siegfried's Youth." Three panels showing Siegfried's preparation to kill the dragon. He begins by having sword made, but stein is humorous because he is shown hitting the dragon with a club. Price: $825.

362. Size: ½ *l*. Description: 2401, etched. "Tannhäuser in the Venusberg." Prince approaches woman sitting up on bed; a servant fans her and a cupid is next to the bed; nice pink color for background. Price: $875.

363. Size: ½ *l*. Description: 2402. etched. "Judging of Siegfried's Worth." Seven figures. Price: $775.

364. Size: ½ *l*. Description: 2441, etched. "Old German Drinkers Playing Dice." Gambling scene with dice, man and woman on each side sitting on floor observing. Price: $650.

365. Size: 2.25 *l*. Description: 2482, etched. "Marksman at Targetshooting Contest." Nine figures, archery scenes, signed *FQ* on ceramic insert lid. Price: $1,350.

366. Size: 1 *l*. Description: 2500, etched. "Drinking, Old German Soldiers." Three men beside keg of beer having their fling. Price: $785.

367. Size: ½ l. Description: 2501, etched. "Scene in Front of the Pub." Drinking in the yard. Seven figures, signed *F. Quidenus*. Price: $575.

368. Size: ½ l. Description: 2520, etched. "Student and Waitress, with Verse." Student sitting at table, waitress, signed *H.S.* Price: $625.

369. Size: ½ l. Description: 2526, relief. "Hunt Scene, Kreussen Style." Price: $600.

370. Size: ½ l. Description: 2528, etched. Six men congratulating winner of a bicycle race, woman delivering trophy, signed *F. Quidenus*. Price: $625.

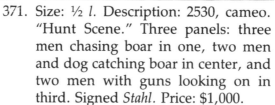

371. Size: ½ l. Description: 2530, cameo. "Hunt Scene." Three panels: three men chasing boar in one, two men and dog catching boar in center, and two men with guns looking on in third. Signed *Stahl*. Price: $1,000.

372. Size: 1 l. Description: 2530, cameo. "Hunt Scene." Very close to ½ l., 2530, except base is larger and includes rabbits and foxes. Also figures are similar but not exact as their positions have changed slightly from those of smaller stein. Price: $1,400.

373. Size:½ l. Description: 2531, etched. "Ahoy, the Air is Fresh and Pure, etc." from Scheffel; man with mandolin, man sitting on porch, man and woman in background, rural scene. Signed *F. Quidenus*. Price: $725.

374. Size: ½ l. Description: 2532, etched. "Drunken Feast." Seven figures drinking, singing and toasting, dinner being served, monkey on floor. Signed *Quidenus*. Price: $600.

375. Size: ½ l. Description: 2556, relief. "Drinking Scene." Three panels: three men standing on one, three men playing cards in center, woman serving beer and man drawing from top in third. White figures against blue. Price: $325.

376. Size: ½ *l.* Description: 2580, etched. "Kannenburg." Large stein with *Prosit*, jester, knight drinking from stein, man and woman, dog, two other knights, signed *Heinrich Schlitt.* Price: $825.

377. Size: 1 *l.* Description: 2582, etched. "Fool's Sermon." Jester addressing eight people, signed *Quidenus.* Price: $1,000.

378. Size: ½ *l.* Description: 2583, etched. Three panels, Egyptian figures in each, humorous theme of man not paying his dinner bill. Price: $750.

379. Size: 1 *l.* Description: 2583, etched. Same as ½ *l.* Price: $925.

380. Size: ½ l. Description: 2585, etched and relief. "Munich Child on Top of Globe." Munich Child in relief is standing on top of globe of world, city of Munich etched in background. Price: $795.

381. Size: ½ l. Description: 2587, etched. Five women: one plays a harp; three with a music sheet are singing; one holds string instrument and bow. Price: $575.

382. Size: ³⁄₁₀ l. Description: 2627, cameo. "Bicyclist." Three scenes, two men in one, man and woman in center and man in third. Green background. Price: $675.

383. Size: ½ l. Description: 2627, cameo. "Bicyclist." Men and woman in bicycle scene, green background. Price: $795.

384. Size: ½ l. Description: 2632, etched. "Bowling." Five people at table observing man bowling. Price: $550.

385. Size: ½ l. Description: 2635, etched. "Girl Bicyclist." Girl standing beside her bicycle, waving. Price: $625.

386. Size: ½ l. Description: 2638, etched. "Girl's Portrait." Pretty girl in oval panel with attractive designs on each side on the body of stein. Price: $585.

387. Size: ½ l. Description: 2639, etched. "Two Drinkers Toasting Brotherhood." Two men with arms entwined are drinking from their steins. Price: $685.

388. Size: ½ l. Description: 2640, etched. "Drinker, with Verse." Cavalier sitting at table while barmaid pours beer into his beaker. Price: $575.

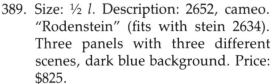

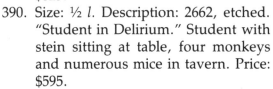

389. Size: ½ *l*. Description: 2652, cameo. "Rodenstein" (fits with stein 2634). Three panels with three different scenes, dark blue background. Price: $825.

390. Size: ½ *l*. Description: 2662, etched. "Student in Delirium." Student with stein sitting at table, four monkeys and numerous mice in tavern. Price: $595.

391. Size: 1.4 *l*. Description: 2682, etched. "Woman Vintner." Young lady picking grapes. Price: $975.

392. Size: ½ *l*. Description: 2693, etched. "Barmaid and Drinker." Tavern scene—barmaid, knight and troubador. Stein has same scene as 2692. Price: $585.

393. Size: ½ *l*. Description: 2714, cameo. "Music and Dance." Three panels, man and woman in each, white on blue background. Price: $775.

394. Size: 1 *l*. Description: 2716, etched. "Drinker with Verse." Two men at table being served by waitress, scene encompassed with wreath, signed *F. Q.* Price: $825.

395. Size: 1 *l*. Description: 2717, etched. "Amor Cupid as Marksman, with Verse." Cupid standing, nearly nude woman with arrow pierced in heart against target background, village scene, rabbits. Price: $925.

396. Size: 1 *l*. Description: 2718, etched. "David and Goliath, with Verse." Body dominated by Goliath, unusual handle with four holes. Price: $2,200.

397. Size: ½ *l*. Description: 2719, etched. Baker occupational. Lions on shield with pretzel, verse. Lid has loaves of bread. Price: Range of $1,000 to $1,800, but a complete set of all twelve could bring minimum of $18,000.

398. Size: ½ *l*. Description: 2720, etched. Tailor occupational. Mounted cavalier is George Baron von Derf-flinger, famous figure in Germany in 1600s who apparantly was also a tailor, verse. Lid shows tools of tailor. Price: Same as 2719.

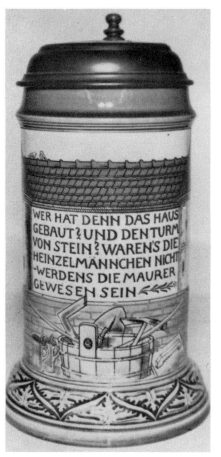

399. Size: ½ l. Description: 2721, etched. Cabinetmaker occupational, body has verse for trade. Lid depicts tools of trade. Price: Same as 2719.

400. Size: ½ l. Description: 2722, etched. Shoemaker occupational. Picture is of Hans Sachs, famous shoemaker and poet in 1500s, verse. Lid depicts jackboot and other tools. Price: Same as 2719.

401. Size: ½ l. Description: 2723, etched. Carpenter occupational. Carpenter and child working, verse. Lid has pine tree. Price: Same as 2719.

402. Size: ½ l. Description: 2724, etched. Mason occupational. Stone wall and tools, mason working on one side and helper on other, verse. Lid has triangle, crown, and compass. Price: Same as 2919.

403. Size: ½ l. description: 2725, etched. Painter occupational. Woman, antlers, and crown on front. Lid has palette and brush, verse. Price: Same as 2719.

404. Size: ½ l. Description: 2726, etched. Goldsmith occupational. A bishop making a gold cup. He is Saint Elegins, patron saint of goldsmiths, who lived in the seventh century. A ciborium on lid. Price: Same as 2719.

405. Size: ½ l. Description: 2727, etched. Printer occupational. Double-headed black eagle. In background is town of Mainz, where first movable type was invented by Johann Gutenberg. Verse on lid. Price: Same as 2719.

406. Size: ½ l. Description: 2728, etched. Brewer occupational. Barrel with tools and hops, verse. Lid has barrel and stein. Price: Same as 2719.

407. Size: ½ l. Description: 2729, etched. Locksmith and smithies occupational. Shields on sides with tools of trades, verse. Lid has vise. Price: Same as 2719.

408. Size: ½ l. Description: 2730, etched. Butcher occupational. Ox with tools of trade, verse. Pig on lid. Price: Same as 2719.

409. Size: 1 *l*. Description: 2745, etched. "To Our Health." Man with pipe and stein of beer enjoying himself. Price: $750.

410. Size: ½ *l*. Description: 2752, etched. "Drinker and Rococo Figures." Two gentlemen sitting at table, drinking. Price: $650.

411. Size: ½ *l*. Description: 2754, cameo. "Pair of Lovers." Man and woman in each of three panels, signed *Stahl*, blue background. Price: $785.

412. Size: ½ *l*. Description: 2755, cameo. "Drinker." Three panels with two men in two panels and a man and woman in third, green background. Price: $770.

413. Size: ½ and 1 *l.* Description: 2765, etched. "Knight." Knight riding white horse while holding sword with right arm, drinking from stein with left arm, nice colors. Price: ½ *l.*, $2,200; 1 *l.*, $3,000.

414. Size: ½ *l.* Description: 2767, etched. "Munich Child," standing next to large barrel, twin towers of Munich in background. Price: $800.

415. Size: ½ *l.* Description: 2776, etched. "Cooper." Boy in cellar raising stein, wearing apron, keys. Price: $700.

416. Size: ¼ *l.* Description: 2778, etched. "Carnival Player and Group of Drinkers." Jester plus seven other figures and dog as he entertains, signed *H. Schlitt.* Price: $575.

417. Size: ½ l. Description: 2778, etched. Same as ¼ l. Price: $1,000.
418. Size: 1 l. Description: 2778, etched. Same as ¼ l. Price: $1,500.
419. Size: 1 l. Description: 2780, etched. "Pair of Lovers." Gentleman playing mandolin for his lady. Price: $775.
420. Size: ½ l. Description: 2789, PUG. "Drinker." Man smoking and drinking, reddish brown background. Price: $450.
421. Size: ½ l. Description: 2791, PUG. "Drinker." Gentleman with stein. Price: $425.

146

422. Size: ¼ l. Description: 2792, PUG. "Drinker." Cavalier with pipe and stein. Price: $340.

423. Size: ½ l. Description: 2798, etched. "Portrait of Richard Wagner." Price: $650.

424. Size: ½ l. Description: 2808, etched. "Bowling." Woman bowling, two men and woman watching. Price: $550.

425. Size: ½ l. Description: 2813, etched. "Modern Hunting Emblems." Skull, acorns, and antlers. According to legend, a nobleman, Hubert, was converted to Christianity when a stag he had chased in the woods spoke to him about joining the church. The stag appeared with a cross of fire between his antlers. This stein depicts the stag who converted Saint Hubert. Price: $475. See Major R. F. Hanson, "Legend of Saint Hubert," *Prosit* (June 1971), p. 125.

426. Size: ½ l. Description: 2828, glazed. "Wartburg." City scenes and forest. Dominant color is green, exceptional lid. Price: $2,000.

427. Size: 1 *l*. Description: 2828, glazed. "Wartburg." Same as ½ *l*. Price: $2,750.

428. Size: ½ *l*. Description: 2829, glazed. "Rodenstein." Housetops of Gersprenz, Odenwald, and Beerfurth, green color dominant, exceptional lid. Price: $2,000.

429. Size: ½ *l*. Description: 2833B, etched. "In the Cool Ground." Men resting in the forest. Price: $450.

430. Size: ½ *l*. Description: 2833D, etched. "Not a Drop Left in the Stein." Man seated at table next to stein, shakes hand of woman. Price: $450.

431. Size: ³⁄₁₀ *l*. Description: 2833E, etched. "I Had a Comrade." Military scene, five soldiers and drummer advancing through woods. Price: $370.

432. Size: ½ l. Description: 2844, etched. Three panels with hunter and deer in one, two men and woman in farm scene in center, and man in boat in third. Price: $625.

433. Size: 1 l. Description: 2871, etched. Cornell University stein, college buildings, song. Price: $1,550.

434. Size: 1 l. Description: 2886, etched. "The Notables." Four men at table with one reading the newspaper, another standing smoking pipe. Price: $750.

435. Size: 1 l. Description: 2888, etched. "Without Care, as the Clouds in the Sky." Three men arm-in-arm, marching happily down a rural road. Price: $750.

436. Size: ½ l. Description: 2894, etched. Panoramic scene of town as young man holds up his goblet. Possibly a student stein, exceptional lid as continuation of body. Price: $1,250.

437. Size: 3 l. Description: 2897/197, PUG. Man and woman by water; boats and windmill provide background. Price: $325.

438. Size: ½ l. Description: 2917, etched. "Munich Child." Three panels with Munich Child in center, lion-shield lid. Price: $1,200.

439. Size: ½ l. Description: 2936, etched. Elk Club stein with elk highlight of etching. Price: $475.

440. Size: ½ l. Description: 2950, cameo. "Bavarian Coat of Arms." Green background. Price: $550.

441. Size: 1 *l.* Description: 2959, etched. "Bowling." Three scenes in stein with someone bowling in each. Price: $650.

442. Size: ½ *l.* Description: 3043, etched and glazed. "The Munich Stein." Price: $1,000.

443. Size: ½ *l.* Description: 3078, Bavaria, etched. Cupid. Price: $450.

444. Size: ½ *l.* Description: 3089, etched. Diogenes sitting in barrel next to his lantern, crow, donkey, signed *Heinrich Schlitt.* This stein is part of a series. Price: $725.

445. Size: 1 *l.* Description: 3089, etched. Same as ½ *l.* Price: $925.

446. Size: 1 *l*. Description: 3090, etched. Man playing guitar with girl on each side, signed *HS* on lid. This stein is part of a series. Price: $850.

447. Size: ½ *l*. Description: 3091, etched. Knight in armor drinking out of large stein, signed *Heinrich Schlitt*. This stein is part of a series. Price: $725.

448. Size: ½ *l*. Description: 3092, etched. Gentleman wearing fez and holding goblet, signed *Heinrich Schlitt*. This stein is part of a series. Price: $650.

449. Size: ½ *l*. Description: 3093, etched. A troll, which is a demon in German mythology. Signed *Heinrich Schlitt*. This stein is part of a series. Price: $650.

450. Size: ½ *l*. Description: 3135, etched. American eagle with flags on each side, nice colors. Price: Too wide a range but likely to be expensive.

451. Size: ½ l. Description: 3156, etched. "Chicago Stein." Masonic Temple in one scene, New County Building in another, Chicago Public Library in third. Mercury on thumblift, freight cars on handle. Price: Too wide a range but likely to be expensive.

452. Size: ½ l. Description: 3252, etched. Two men and woman with feathers in hats, all raising steins. Price: $525.

453. Size: ½ l. Description: 5004, faience. Price: $475.

454. Size: 1 l. Description: 5019/5442, PUG. Cavalier sitting on keg, holding stein, smoking pipe, Price: $650.

455. Size: 1 l. Description: 5022 VB, faience, ship scene. Price: $750.

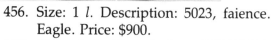

456. Size: 1 *l.* Description: 5023, faience. Eagle. Price: $900.

457. Size: 1 *l.* Description: 5024/5394, faience. Mercury and Pegasus. Price: $1,000.

458. Size: ½ *l.* Description: 5043/965, faience. Price: $490.

459. Size: ½ *l.* Description: 5188, PUG. Gentleman smoking pipe while drinking. Price: $500.

460. Size: ½ *l.* Description: 5190/5015. Gentleman, possibly Falstaff, drinking from goblet. Price: $500.

Mettlach Beakers

461. Size: ¼ l. Description: 2327/1023, 1024, 1025, PUG. *Left*, man playing violin; *center*, man playing flute; *right*, waitress. Price: $75 each.

462. Size: ¼ l. Description: 2327/1139, 1141, PUG. *Left*, man playing fiddle; *right*, gentleman seated and barmaid. Price: *left*, $75; *right*, $75.

463. Size: ¼ l. Description: 2327/1170, 1171, and 1173, PUG. Dwarfs. Price: $80 each.

464. Size: ¼ l. Description: 2327/235, 2368/1014, PUG. *Left*, old man playing guitar; *right*, Munich Child. Price: *left*, $70; *right*, $80.

465. Size: ¼ l. Description: 2368/1032, 1033, PUG, drinking scene in each. Price: $75 each.

466. Size: ¼ *l.* Description: 2368/1091, 1093, 1092, PUG. *Left,* young man playing mandolin; *middle,* young man toasting; *right,* barmaid serving with tray, stein and goblets. Price: $75 each.

467. Size: ¼ *l.* Description: 2842/1175, 1172, PUG. Dwarfs, unusually shaped beakers. Price: $95 each.

468. Size: ¼ *l.* Description: 2954/1194, PUG. Goblet, cherubs. Price: $150 each.

Ornate Steins

469. Size: ½ *l.* Description: Royal Vienna, religious scene. Lid has scenes on each side. Beehive mark under base, exceptional colors. Price: $1,200 to $1,500.

470. Size: 2 *l.* Description: Ivory, battle scene with Joan of Arc, circa 1700–1750. Price: Very high.

471. Size: ½ *l.* Description: Ivory, figures include woman, young children, and a man, circa 1850. Price: Expensive.

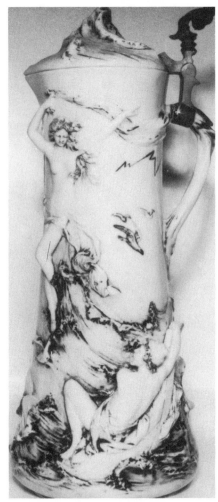

472. Size: 1 *l*. Description: Capo-di-monte, military scene, *N* and crown mark under base, nice colors. Price: $1,200.

473. Size: ½ *l*. Description: Meissen, porcelain, Lorelei stein, blue and white, marked *378* under base. Price: $700.

474. Size: ½ *l*. Description: Lead stein, dated 1871, satire with French fighting Germans as theme represented by dwarfs. Price: The stein is unique, and the price cannot be determined.

Glossary

BEAKER. A drinking vessel without a lid or handle, usually ¼ liter in size.

CAMEO. Raised white design that is translucent; usually on green or blue background. New theories indicate process was completed through identical mold rather than application of white from another mold.

CHARACTER STEIN. A figural stein depicting a person, animal, vegetable, or object.

ETCHED. Design incised or engraved into body of stein. Artisans used black paint to fill in lines and other colors to complete motif.

FAIENCE. Earthenware of clay fired at a low temperature and covered with a tin oxide glaze which prepared stein for hand painting by an artist. Many of these steins appeared in the seventeenth through nineteenth centuries and are unique because they are handcrafted.

GAMBRINUS. Mythological king (or founder) of beer who appears on many steins as central figure.

GESETZLICH GESCHÜTZT. "Protected by law"; appearing on the underside of the base of a stein, indicates that the design is registered or patented.

KREUSSEN. Seventeenth-century handmade steins coated with brown glaze; many appear with raised figures of various colors. These steins were reproduced over the years and collectors may be easily fooled unless they are familiar with the early ones made in Kreussen, Germany.

LITER. Metric unit of measure equal to 33.8 oz. Most steins were made in the half-liter size, but come as small as ⅛ liter and as large as seven liters.

LITHOPHANE. A translucent picture in porcelain that is visible when held up to a light; produced by using varying thicknesses of clay. Many steins have a lithophane base that can be viewed by lifting the lid and looking through the inside of the stein. These lithophane bottoms were often supplied to the stein producers by manufacturers who specialized in this art.

MARK. German unit of currency equal to twenty-five cents around 1900. The best half-liter steins produced by Villeroy and Boch around 1900 cost about one dollar and twenty-five cents, or five marks.

METTLACH. A type of stein produced in Mettlach, Germany, by the manufacturer Villeroy and Boch.

MOSAIC. A surface decorated by laying small pieces of material to create a pattern or design; some steins have a mosaic effect.

MUNICH MAID (*MÜNCHNER KINDL*). The traditional symbol of Munich; first appeared in the sixteenth century, having evolved from earlier characters who appeared as monks. She is the most popular figure on steins, appearing throughout the centuries of stein making.

MUSTERSCHUTZ. "Registered design"; appearing on the underside of the base of a stein, indicates that the design is registered or patented. This mark is found mostly on porcelain character steins along with the hash mark (#).

OCCUPATIONAL STEINS. Steins depicting the occupation of the owner. A slogan or the owner's name may also appear on the stein.

POKAL. A drinking vessel usually larger in size than a beaker (¼ liter) without a handle; it has a cover but no hinge. Villeroy and Boch produced excellent pokals in the late 1800s.

PORCELAIN. Material made of a kaolin, quartz, and feldspar fired at a high temperature. Porcelain first appeared in China in the sixteenth century and in Germany in the early eighteenth. It became popular in stein manufacturing in the nineteenth and twentieth centuries.

PRINT UNDER GLAZE (PUG). Process in which the design is placed on the body of the stein by a transfer method from a copper plate.

PROSIT. Traditional German toast (also *Prost*) and the name of the quarterly journal of Stein Collectors International.

REGIMENTAL STEIN. A type of stein manufactured for German reservists; usually purchased after discharge from military. Such steins usually depict the branch of service, and most have unit members' names on the body along with the owner's name.

RELIEF. Decoration made in a separate mold and applied to the body of the stein, giving the piece a raised effect.

SALT GLAZE. Glaze produced when salt is put into kiln when the firing is at its highest temperature. Blue is the most common color.

STEIN. A drinking vessel with a handle and an attached lid; known in Germany as a *Krug*. The use of a lid dates back to the fifteenth century and differentiates the stein from the mug.

TAPESTRY. Usually steins decorated in this manner have plain bodies and are made to look as though a small tapestry has been nailed onto the front. The tapestry has an etched design superimposed on it.

TURNVEREIN or 4F. Athletic society founded by Frederick Ludwig Jahn around 1811 in Germany. The symbol of the society is 4F, which stands for *frisch, fromm, froh,* and *frei,* meaning "fresh," "loyal," "happy," and "free." Steins with the 4F symbol were popular in Germany.

VILLEROY AND BOCH. Company formed in the nineteenth century that became famous for its Mettlach steins, which were made in its factory at Mettlach. The production of steins stopped around 1932 but began again in 1976. The company also produces dinnerware and related products.

Bibliography

Clarke, Pat, and Lowenstein, Jack G. *English Translation: 1899 Mettlach Catalogue with Supplement Steins.* Princeton, N.J.: Patrick J. Clarke and Jack G. Lowenstein, 1974.

Dimsdle, June. *Steins and Prices.* Kansas City, Mo.: Old World Antiques, 1970.

Harrell, John L. *Regimental Steins.* Frederick, Md.: Old Soldiers Press, 1979.

Henschen, Roland. "The Stein Makers." *Tri-State Trader.* Knightstown, Ind.: Mayhill Publications, 1971–76.

Manusov, Eugene. *Encyclopedia of Character Steins.* Des Moines, Iowa: Wallace-Homestead Book Co., 1976.

Mohr, R. H. *Mettlach Steins and Their Prices.* Rockford, Ill.: R. H. Mohr, 1978.

Post, Anton. *Villeroy and Boch 1885/Mettlach 1905.* Wheeling, Ill.: Hans J. Ammelounx, 1975.

Prosit. Quarterly journal of steins published by Stein Collectors International, Kingston, N.J.

Thomas, Thérèse. *Keramik.* Triesen/Liechtenstein, West Germany: Buchverlag J. Bückel, 1978.

Wald, Mike. *HR Steins.* Kingston, N.J.: S.C.I. Publications, 1980.

Index